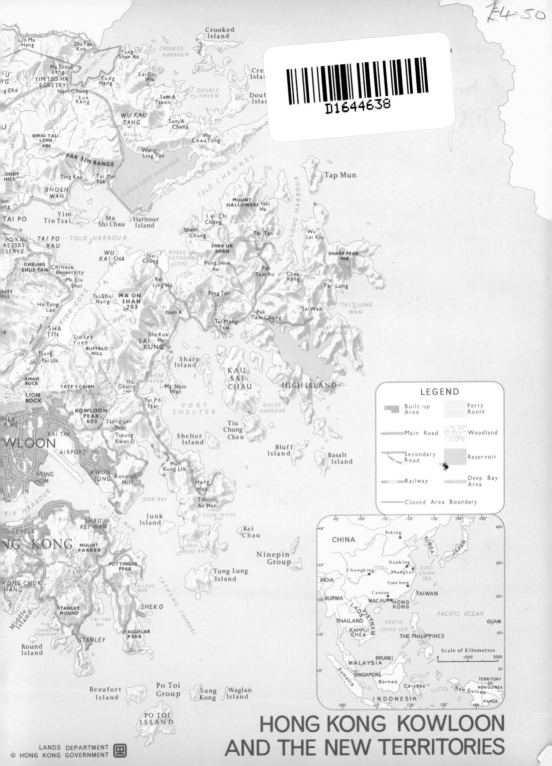

HONG KONG KOWLOON
AND THE NEW TERRITORIES

LEGEND

Built-up Area
Ferry Route
Main Road
Woodland
Secondary Road
Reservoir
Railway
Deep Bay Area
Closed Area Boundary

A COLOUR GUIDE TO
HONG KONG
BIRDS

Clive Viney
Karen Phillipps

Printed and Published by the Government Printer, Hong Kong

"When Hongkong was ceded to Great Britain it was a bare rocky island, such as line the coast of South-East China, and the resident land birds of the colony must nearly all be immigrants which have gradually found their way to the magnificent woods and luxuriant vegetation due to the efforts of the Hongkong Forestry Department."

J. D. D. La Touche – 1934
(A Handbook of the Birds of
Eastern China – Volume II)

First Edition: December, 1977

Second Edition: November, 1979

CONTENTS

Introduction

This book has been designed to illustrate in colour all the birds of Hong Kong that are likely to be seen. The paintings and supporting text should provide ready identification of any bird seen, be it on a casual stroll around Victoria Peak or on a visit to the fabulous Mai Po Marshes.

The main body of the book covers all resident species, regular and occasional visitors with a few of the more striking stragglers included for good measure. An appendix lists the extreme rarities. Additionally, information is given on good bird watching areas, how to identify and watch birds and on equipment to use.

The text

ARRANGEMENT. The birds are generally arranged by families approximately following the accepted scientific order. However, this is adjusted so that the first nineteen plates depict larger species (*non-passeriformes*) associated with water and water-side habitats. Smaller birds (*passeriformes*) which favour wetland areas, such as Great Reed Warbler and Red-Throated Pipit follow in the correct order with other members of their respective families. Notes of general family characteristics precede many of the individual species descriptions.

NAMES. English names used are those generally accepted in Hong Kong. Where more than one name is familiar this is given in parentheses. The scientific and Chinese names are those employed in *An Annotated Check List of the Birds of Hong Kong* (1975) by M. A. Webster, published by the Hong Kong Bird Watching Society.

SIZE. In the interests of conformity the sizes given correspond to those quoted in *A Field Guide to the Birds of South-East Asia* (1975) by Ben King, Martin Woodcock and E. C. Dickenson. This is the length of the bird from the tip of the bill to the tip of the tail with neck outstretched. Sizes often look shorter in the field as the neck is normally curved. Inches have been retained as metric units are only just becoming vogue in Hong Kong.

STATUS. Some birds are resident or present in Hong Kong throughout the year (including introduced species). A few arrive in spring to breed, leaving in autumn. Others come to spend the winter months in what is to them a warmer climate or better feeding ground. Yet others are passage migrants which only visit Hong Kong in spring and autumn on their way to breeding grounds elsewhere. Certain species occur only irregularly, perhaps at intervals of several years, and these are described as occasional visitors. Vagrants are stragglers which have only very rarely wandered to Hong Kong. Finally, the keeping of cagebirds in Hong Kong is very popular and certain species are often seen flying free. The most regularly recorded of these are listed as escapes. The specific status of each species is given after its size, followed in the case of visitors by the period when it is most likely to be seen.

For species occurring annually the following symbols prefix the English name:—

● Widespread and common. Should be seen (or at least heard) annually by even the most sedentary bird watcher.

◉ Local but not uncommon. If species' favoured habitat is visited at the appropriate time of year, should be seen annually.

○ Very local or rare. Usually occurs annually in very small numbers or restricted to a particular locality. Also includes irruption species which may be common and widespread in some years but absent in others.

An asterisk (*) after a species' status indicates that breeding has been proved in Hong Kong.

CHARACTERISTICS. The text stresses plumage points which are the most important for identification and enable separation from other similar species in the field. Space has not permitted the illustration of all female, immature and seasonal plumages and where appropriate these are briefly described. If a bird has a known distinctive call or song this is given but is often difficult to put satisfactorily into words. The best advice is to learn calls and songs with an experienced observer. Other characteristics which aid identification, such as flight behaviour and feeding techniques are included.

HABITAT. This describes the type of area where a bird is most often found and is usually a necessary clue for identification. Most species are very particular about their choice of breeding habitat but outside of the breeding season can be found in quite different areas. Habitat preferences are given in the text and for the less widespread species specific reference as to where it occurs in Hong Kong is mentioned. Place names have been kept to a minimum and can all be found on the maps on the inside covers. Details of the more important areas are included in the section 'Where to Watch Birds in Hong Kong.'

Additionally, a simple habitat key has been devised and follows each species' entry, viz:—

♠ Any built-up areas, urban parks and gardens, cemeteries and playing fields.

♠ Afforested areas and other woodland, ie. areas with a continuous cover of trees with interlocking canopies.

※ Cultivated areas (except flooded paddy land), includes market gardening land, crop land and the scattered trees, shrubs, fallowed and abandoned land found within these areas.

△ Scrubland. Land with a fairly continuous cover of shrubs and bushes from three to ten feet in height and including occasional higher scattered trees found within these areas.

⁂ Grassland. Very low vegetation, not usually exceeding three feet in height, or bare ground. Includes most upland areas, grazing land, rice stubble and overgrown reclaimed land.

≋ Reservoirs, fish-ponds, streams, water catchments, reed beds, flooded paddy land, swampy areas and their immediate surrounds.

⌇ The seaside. Beaches, sandy or muddy, rocky coastline, tidal creeks, mangroves, inlets and open sea.

DB Denotes a species which occurs mainly in the Deep Bay area and not usually seen elsewhere in Hong Kong.

← Denotes a species invariably seen in the air (rarely at rest) over a variety of habitats.

The habitats shown in the text indicate main preferences although it is possible to find a species in quite unexpected areas, particularly during migration.

OTHER NOTES. A few brief notes provide breeding details (where known) and information of interest in the context of Hong Kong and China.

How to identify birds

GENERAL. Firstly, be patient and don't expect to identify every bird that you see. Often only a quick glimpse of colour is permitted and failure to identify can be most frustrating, but once interest has been aroused this will only serve as a stimulus to press on and find other birds. Certain female and immature plumages are confusing and sometimes specific identification is not possible despite an excellent view.

In the text 33 species are prefixed by ● indicating that they are common and widespread. Learn the characteristics of these species and be able to identify them at a glance and in this way the common birds can be eliminated before the rarities are considered.

Learn to be quiet. Don't plunge noisily through the undergrowth or chatter continuously to a colleague. Whilst some species perch prominently and are apparently oblivious to noise others, particularly in woodland, are wary and only seen with great effort.

Try to go out with somebody more knowledgeable but don't just rely on his identification; be sure you understand how he identifies the bird e.g. its prominent crest, red vent or distinctive call. An excellent start in this respect is to join the Hong Kong Bird Watching Society. This Society publishes an important annual report in the form of a systematic list, circulates regular bulletins containing up to the minute information on local birds as well as articles on almost any aspect of ornithology and holds field trips throughout the cooler months. Absolute beginners are welcome and field trips are always provided with an experienced leader. Recently, Chinese-speaking outings have been held to encourage local members. Visitors to Hong Kong can usually be accommodated on field trips and members can be contacted through the Hong Kong Tourist Association. The address of the society is:—

> Hong Kong Bird Watching Society
> c/o Zoology Department
> University of Hong Kong
> Hong Kong

EQUIPMENT. Binoculars are essential. Buy the best that you can afford as, apart from providing a clearer view, eyestrain will be kept to a minimum. Long days in the field can be tiring enough but a headache from eyestrain caused by using poor binoculars can spoil an otherwise excellent outing.

The best all round magnification is X 8 but in woodland and for general use X 7 is acceptable. In open areas such as marshland and on the coast a higher magnification is useful, but never greater than X 10 as such binoculars cannot be held steady enough for bird watching without a tripod. The diameter of the object lens is most important and is quoted after the magnification, e.g. 7 x 40 or 10 x 50. This represents the light gathering power. A key figure is obtained by dividing the magnification into the diameter, e.g. 7 into 40 goes 6 (near enough) or 10 into 50 goes 5, and any result between 4 and 7 is satisfactory. Most binoculars have a field of view marked on them and this should be as wide as possible but decreases with magnification. Another very important consideration, one which is often overlooked, is the minimum focusing distance and this can easily be tested when purchasing. Nothing is more frustrating than to have a magnificent flycatcher or flowerpecker, for example, a few feet away and to be unable to focus your binoculars upon it. Obviously, the shorter the minimum focusing distance the better. A further simple test when buying binoculars is to focus them on a distant object against the sky, such as a flagpole, and ensure that there are no colour fringes around the object. Some binoculars have tinted lenses. These are not really suitable for bird watching. Never point binoculars anywhere near the sun as this can cause immediate blindness.

A final point to consider when buying binoculars is weight. With standard prismatic binoculars the higher the magnification usually the heavier the weight. A pair of standard prismatic 10 x 50 binoculars can seem very heavy towards the end of a day in the field compared with a pair of lightweight, but very expensive, 10 x 40 'roof prism' binoculars.

Telescopes are an optional extra but are generally for the specialist looking for rare shorebirds on distant mudflats or at ducks far out to sea. They are mostly heavy and require tripods to be used comfortably. Magnifications of X 30 up to X 60 are the most usual. Good, worthwhile telescopes are expensive.

Always take a small notebook and one or two pencils. If you can afford it a pocket tape recorder is ideal. Dress sombrely and wear a sun hat. If out for a long day in the warmer months in Hong Kong take plenty to drink and, if susceptible to mosquitoes, a suitable repellent.

'Tickers' or 'listers' are much maligned by the more professional ornithologists but I believe everybody who gets the bird watching bug keeps a list or some record of what he sees. If you have taken the trouble to make field notes write them up in the evening and keep a record. It will certainly add to the pleasure which bird watching can give.

TAKING NOTES. Before venturing forth it is best to be able to refer to the various parts of a bird. It is not necessary to memorise all the scientific names for the various parts of a bird's anatomy but at least use a personal shorthand that can later on be related to the illustrations. The following points should be noted for identification:—
1. *Size and shape.* Six well known birds that can be used for comparison in order of size are White-Eye (a common enough cagebird), Tree Sparrow, Chinese Bulbul, Spotted Dove, Greater Coucal and Black Kite. Birds associated with

water generally have distinctive shapes, e.g. shorebirds, rails, ducks, gulls and herons.

2. *General colouration.* Above and below.
3. *Conspicuous marks or patches.* Note their colour and approximate position on the bird.
4. *Size and shape of bill, legs, wings, tail and neck.*
5. *Colour of bill, legs, feet and eyes.*
6. *Characteristics of flight or actions,* e.g. tail wagging of wagtails or hovering of a Kestrel.
7. *Distinctive call notes or song.* Often difficult to express but some calls such as those of the Greater Coucal or Chinese Francolin are unmistakable.
8. *Comparison with any other birds.* A brown bird wagging its tail like a wagtail may well be an Indian Tree Pipit.
9. *Date, time, place and weather.* Often good clues to identification.
10. *Habitat and general surroundings.* The text key will help to eliminate unlikely species although birds can occasionally turn up in quite unexpected places.
11. *Angle of vision, condition of light and distance from observer.* Poor light or an odd angle can play very peculiar tricks.

When analysing field notes later on do not forget to consider the possibilities of albinism, melanism (partial or otherwise) and the fact that the bird may have been damaged, e.g. tail feathers missing or abraded feathers causing pale patches.

If you are really unable to identify a distinctive bird, of which a good view was obtained and full notes taken, then write to the Hong Kong Bird Watching Society and they will do their best to find an answer. Every year new birds to Hong Kong are recorded and not always on the Deep Bay Marshes.

Where to watch birds in Hong Kong

Like most places birds can be found almost anywhere in Hong Kong. Obviously the number of species in urban districts is limited but it is possible to see most of the commoner birds in the green areas of the city, such as the Botanical Gardens, Colonial Cemetery at Happy Valley and especially along some of the quieter stretches of Mid-Levels like Bowen Road. The better known walks around Victoria Peak are often disappointing during the middle of the day, but in early morning are a much better prospect.

Away from the urban districts it is best, initially, to visit an area of open country which has mixed agriculture, scrubland and 'fung shui' woods such as the Lam Tsuen Valley. Here many species of commoner birds are readily seen with a real chance of one or two rarities.

During the breeding season a visit to the spectacular egretry at Yim Tso Ha is an absolute must. Up to one thousand egrets, many in full plumage, can be seen there at the height of the season.

Certain localities are referred to time and time again in the main text and these are the areas the enthusiast should not miss. The Mai Po Marshes, truly unique and of international importance, the Tai Po Kau Forestry Reserve with its well-marked paths and the Mong Tseng Peninsula which offers almost every type of habitat.

However, I cannot emphasize enough that much of Hong Kong remains to be explored, ornithologically speaking, and recent field trips to areas like Tai Long Wan on the Sai Kung Peninsula have shown tremendous potential.

Details of the better known localities and how to get there are given below. Anybody relying on public transport should first check the details with the Kowloon Motor Bus Co. Ltd. or the Hong Kong Tourist Association. Excellent maps (some showing current bus numbers) are available from the Map Sales Division of the Crown Lands and Survey Office, Murray Building (19/F); the Government Bookshop and the Hong Kong Tourist Association. The better maps have to be purchased but only cost a few dollars and are excellent value.

MAI PO MARSHES. This is a restricted area and entry is only possible by permit obtainable from the Agriculture and Fisheries Department, Canton Road Government Offices, 393 Canton Road, Kowloon, Hong Kong.

By car, go via Route Twisk through Kam Tin turning northwards at Au Tau (about a mile east of Yuen Long) and proceed to Mai Po Village. Just before a sharp right bend on the main road turn left (westwards) onto a single track road alongside a fish garden and restaurant and continue to the end of the road below Tam Kon Chau Police Post where there is a small car park.

By bus there is a regular service from Tai Kok Tsui Ferry Terminus (Kowloon) to Au Tau where a bus connection can be made to Mai Po Village. Public light buses go regularly to Yuen Long from Jordan Road Ferry Terminus (Kowloon) where the bus to Mai Po can also be caught. It is about a mile walk from Mai Po to Tam Kon Chau but along a quiet road through fish-ponds where many of the commoner waterside birds can be seen.

Follow the footpath onto the main marsh (past the signboard) and through a row of huts where you will be stopped by a warden and asked to show your permit and sign in. The best route is to continue along the main bund southward, exploring any of the subsidiary bunds running generally westward where the water-level is low and attractive to shorebirds. If the main bund is followed round it eventually turns west and then northward along the edge of the mangrove swamp. Do not be tempted to enter the mangroves as the mud is treacherous and the tide comes in rapidly. This bund can be followed to a point about a half mile south of a prominent rocky outcrop where a signboard marks the limit of the Border Closed Area. Do not enter this area for to do so is a serious offence. At this point, your movements will probably be closely monitored by the police at the Tam Kon Chau Police Post. By back-tracking a short way, one of the bunds running inland will take you back to a point about a half mile south of your entry. Clearly, it is best to tackle this vast area with an experienced guide or on an organised Hong Kong Bird Watching Society Outing.

What you see will depend much on the time of year and the water-level. Generally the migrations are very good, particularly spring but at any time these marshes are impressive.

LOK MA CHAU. Proceed as to Mai Po Village (above) but continue along the main road by bus or car to the junction of Lok Ma Chau Road. Either side of this road to the Lookout and Police Post can be good, particularly during the migrations. There are shallow fish-ponds and marshland extending towards San Tin on the western side and an area of damp rough grazing to the east.

LONG VALLEY AND HO SHEUNG HEUNG. Proceed as to Lok Ma Chau Road (above) but continue along the main road by car or bus to Dill's Corner (about $1\frac{1}{2}$ miles) then turn north towards Crest Hill to Lo Wu Camp. This is the best area for raptors in Hong Kong, particularly eagles in winter but has suffered much from disturbance in recent years. Before reaching Lo Wu Camp a road branches east to Ho Sheung Heung which has a magnificent 'fung shui' wood. This wood has produced some splended rarities.

MONG TSENG PENINSULA. By car drive to Ping Shan (about a mile west of Yuen Long) either via Castle Peak Road or over Route Twisk. At Ping Shan take the road branching north-westwards to Lau Fau Shan (Sha Kong Tsuen) and at the roundabout turn right to Tsim Bei Tsui.

Tsim Bei Tsui is an excellent point to watch Deep Bay in winter for seabirds including pelicans. Any of the numerous tracks between the roundabout at Lau Fau Shan and Tsim Bei Tsui are worth exploring. This road is not particularly busy and a good number of species can be recorded whilst walking its length. South of Lau Fau Shan (turn left at the roundabout) is a road, rough in places, which follows the coast to Nim Wan. Along this road are excellent vantage points for watching terns and gulls in winter. Again it is as well explored on foot as in a car.

TAI PO KAU FORESTRY RESERVE. By car follow the Tai Po Road to the Reserve entrance (an obvious lay-by at milestone 42) where there is ample parking space. By bus there are regular services from Tai Kok Tsui and Jordan Road Ferry Terminals (Kowloon).

There are several clearly marked walks of distances to suit your stamina (see detailed notice board at the dam). The 'blue walk' is considered best for birds as it offers more open vistas, but much depends on luck. Patience and stealth are required to see anything at all but rarities occur, particularly during winter irruptions. Avoid mid-summer (too hot) and Sundays.

SHEK KONG WOODS. By car drive to Shek Kong over Route Twisk turning left at the junction then shortly left again at the junction of Lam Kam Road where there is a small car park next to a playground. A bus goes regularly from Tai Kok Tsui Ferry Terminus (Kowloon) to Shek Kong.

The woods lie between Lam Kam Road and Kam Tin Road and are interspersed with farmland and a particularly polluted stream, which nevertheless attracts birds (notably thrushes). This is a difficult area to find your way around and is best visited with somebody who knows the district.

LAM TSUEN VALLEY. Proceed to Shek Kong (as above) but turn right at the junction (north-eastwards) over the hill and down into the Lam Tsuen Valley. A bus runs through the valley from Shek Kong to Tai Po.

This is open cultivated country with good 'fung shui' woods, particularly at Tai Om and She Shan. Both these villages are on the south-east side of the road and are signposted. It is best to skirt around the perimeter of the woods rather than attempt to penetrate them. On the upper slopes of the valley streams run down from Tai Mo Shan and, although promising, these areas have rarely been visited by bird watchers.

TAI MO SHAN. At the top of Route Twisk (en route to Shek Kong) turn east up a road which climbs to the summit of Tai Mo Shan. Stop at a barrier where there is a small car park. The barrier may be passed only on foot. This is the best area for Hong Kong's few montane species. Hopeless in mist but cool and often worthwhile in summer.

YIM TSO HA EGRETRY. By car follow the Tai Po Road to the Fanling roundabout and turn right towards Sha Tau Kok. About a half mile before the Border Closed Area barrier turn sharp right along a road which follows the shore of Starling Inlet. The egretry is on a small hill near this junction and cannot be missed during the breeding season.

By bus there is a regular service from Jordan Road Ferry Terminal (Kowloon) to Fanling where a bus connection can be made (at a short distance along Sha Tau Kok Road) to Starling Inlet.

A visit between April and July is an unforgettable experience.

TAI LONG WAN, SAI KUNG PENINSULA. Either drive or take the train to Tai Po Kau Station and board the Tolo Harbour Ferry. This ferry leaves very early in the morning but connects with the first train from Hung Hom. Disembark at Chek Keng and follow the concrete path to Tai Long Wan where there is a magnificent but un-guarded beach, climbing Sharp Peak en route if you wish. Return to Chek Keng to catch the late afternoon ferry.

This is very much an unknown area but a recent trip in October proved very good, particularly for raptors and rare migrants. The scenery is superb.

COLONIAL CEMETERY, HAPPY VALLEY, HONG KONG ISLAND. Take a taxi to the upper entrance off Stubbs Road (the lower entrance is at present through a maze of road construction works for the Aberdeen Tunnel). About fifteen minutes from Central. A good area to learn the characteristics of Hong Kong's common birds but also known for flycatchers.

BOWEN ROAD, HONG KONG ISLAND. Runs along Mid-Levels and for the most part is not open to vehicular traffic. Within easy reach of Central and is a splendid walk not only for common birds but for excellent views of Hong Kong Harbour as well.

Calendar

JANUARY TO MARCH.
Open country areas hold the regular wintering species such as wagtails, pipits, buntings and chats. In the wooded areas warblers and thrushes are found with the real chance of a rare irruption species during very cold weather. Gulls are much in evidence along the coast and at Deep Bay pelicans and duck can be seen.

APRIL AND MAY.
The spring passage. Perhaps the best time to visit the Deep Bay area for shorebirds and terns. Migrating flycatchers are found in the woodlands. The breeding season is in full swing for resident species and summer visitors such as cuckoos and orioles have arrived.

JUNE AND JULY.
Hot, humid and often wet months but a good time to visit the Yim Tso Ha Egretry and Tai Mo Shan.

AUGUST TO OCTOBER.
The autumn passage begins about the middle of August and continues until early November. Like the spring, a good time to visit the Deep Bay area for shorebirds, terns and the chance of seeing the really unexpected. Woodlands hold migrating flycatchers and warblers.

NOVEMBER AND DECEMBER.
Excellent months for walking and therefore a good time to visit rural areas to see resident birds and the return of wintering species which are often in flocks and easy to see. The Deep Bay area holds many herons, egrets, duck, raptors and a few shorebirds at this time.

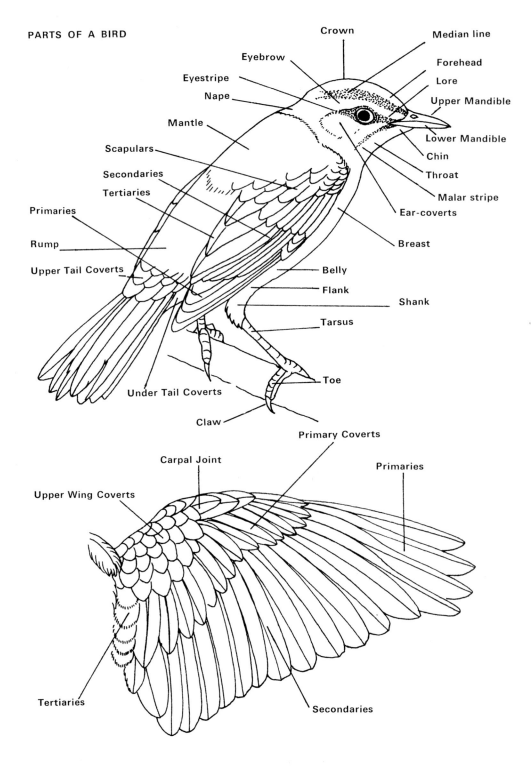

PARTS OF A BIRD

Crown
Median line
Eyebrow
Forehead
Eyestripe
Lore
Nape
Upper Mandible
Mantle
Lower Mandible
Scapulars
Chin
Secondaries
Throat
Tertiaries
Malar stripe
Primaries
Ear-coverts
Rump
Breast
Upper Tail Coverts
Belly
Flank
Shank
Tarsus
Under Tail Coverts
Toe
Claw

Carpal Joint
Primary Coverts
Primaries
Upper Wing Coverts

Tertiaries
Secondaries

Glossary of terms used in the main text

Axillaries	the 'armpits,' where the wing joins the body (seen in flight).
Carpal joint	the joint of the forewing.
Cheeks	the general area of the ear-coverts.
Coronal stripe	a stripe along the centre of the crown.
Ear-coverts	an area of feathers immediately behind the eye.
Eclipse plumage	adopted by male duck after the breeding season, usually similar to female plumage.
Eye-stripe	a stripe through the eye.
Facial skin	a patch of bare skin, usually between the bill and eye.
Feral species	a domesticated species released and living wild.
Flanks	sides of the body appearing just below the wing at rest.
Frontal shield	a prominent raised patch of hardened skin from the base of the upper mandible across the forehead, often brightly coloured.
'Fung shui' woods	small established woods behind villages in the New Territories.
Gorget	a necklace across the throat.
Gular pouch	an expandable patch of bare skin on the throat of pelicans and cormorants.
Immature	denotes all plumage phases except the adult.
Irruption species	an irregularly occurring species which sometimes arrives in large numbers, particularly during hard weather.
Lappets	folds of skin hanging from the head.
Malar stripe	a stripe extending downwards from the base of the bill.
Mantle	back, wing-coverts and scapulars.
Melanistic	blackish.
Moustache stripe	as malar stripe.
Nape	the back of the head where it joins the neck.
Non-passerines	refers to those species having a different foot structure from the passerines. The birds depicted on the first twenty-seven plates are mostly non-passerines.
Orbital skin	skin on the region around the eye.
Passerines	perching birds
Plume	a narrow elongated feather, usually typical of breeding plumage; e.g. egrets.
Primaries	main flight feathers on the wing.
Rump	lower end of back just above the tail.
Scapulars	feathers growing near the joint of wing and body.
Secondaries	feathers at the back of the inner half of the wing.
Speculum	a coloured area on the secondaries.
Sub-adult	a later immature plumage phase.
Tail-coverts	small feathers covering the base of the tail.
Tertials	elongated feathers between the secondaries and the body.
Underparts	under surface of body from throat to vent.
Upperparts	upper surface of body including upper surfaces of wings and tail.
Vagrant	very rare in occurrence.
Vent	the area under the base of the tail.
Wing bars	bands formed on the wings when the tips of the wing-coverts are a different colour from their bases.
Wing-coverts	feathers covering the bases of the primaries and secondaries.
Wing lining	under wing-coverts.

BREEDING HERONS AND EGRETS

Large long-legged wading birds found mainly in the damper areas of the northern New Territories. Wings broad and rounded. Neck long and tucked back in flight. Rounded short tail. The colour of the bill, legs and feet are important points for identification. On migration, fly in large flocks often in V formation. Breed colonially in egretries, principally at Yim Tso Ha near Sha Tau Kok and behind Mai Po village. Nests are built of sticks placed in trees. The breeding season extends from late March until early September. Usually three to six eggs per clutch. The 'white egrets' were greatly persecuted in the late nineteenth century, their beautiful filiform plumes being used for personal adornment. Egrets were in great danger of becoming extinct but fashions changed and persecution has now apparently ceased. Most species have recovered but Swinhoe's Egret remains on the verge of extinction.

CHINESE POND-HERON *Ardeola bacchus* 池鷺
18". Local resident*. Breeding plumage unmistakable. In winter rather nondescript but white wings (invisible at rest) betray them when taking flight. Immatures resemble winter birds. Common in low-lying parts of the New Territories, particularly the north. Numbers increase in summer and between 50 and 100 pairs usually breed. Nesting sites chosen are comparatively low, often in thick cover and together at one end of the egretry.

LITTLE EGRET *Egretta garzetta* 白鷺
24". Local resident*. Entirely white with black bill and distinctive yellow feet which are clearly seen in flight. Plumes are lost in winter and are not present on immatures. Common in low-lying parts of the New Territories, particularly the north, and is only seen elsewhere during migration. Between 50 and 100 pairs usually breed. Since 1973 a single grey-phase bird has occasionally been seen at Mai Po and it is interesting to note that mysterious grey Little Egrets were reported from China early this century (La Touche).

CATTLE EGRET *Bubulcus ibis* 牛背鷺
20". Local resident*. Breeding plumage unmistakable. In non-breeding plumage, stubby yellow bill and bulgy chin separates it from other 'white egrets.' Found in drier areas, often associating with cattle on whose backs it is commonly seen perched. Common in summer in the northern New Territories but is much scarcer and local in winter when it is best seen at Lok Ma Chau. Only found elsewhere on migration. In most years over 100 pairs breed.

SWINHOE'S EGRET (CHINESE EGRET) *Egretta eulophotes* 黃嘴白鷺
27". Summer visitor*. (March to July). Entirely white but distinguished by blue facial skin. Best located fishing along the tideline around Starling Inlet. Two or three pairs now breed at Yim Tso Ha in most years. First discovered breeding near Yuen Long in 1956 and at that time as many as ten pairs bred. This is one of the world's rarest birds and is listed in the Red Data Book of Endangered Species of the International Union for the Conservation of Nature and Natural Resources. The last stronghold of this species is thought to be South China but it may well be close to extinction. Hong Kong is perhaps the best place in the world to still see this egret but even here it is scarce.

GREAT EGRET *Egretta alba* 大白鷺
35". Local resident*. Entirely white but clearly largest of the 'white egrets.' Common winter visitor to the Mai Po Marshes. Single pairs have bred annually at Yim Tso Ha in recent years. It is only found elsewhere on migration. DB

[LESSER EGRET *Egretta intermedia* 中白鷺
not illustrated
28". Occasional visitor. Similar to Great Egret but is smaller and has a stubby bill usually with a black tip and dark base. The few records are mostly restricted to the Deep Bay area in winter. DB]

NIGHT HERON *Nycticorax nycticorax* 夜鷺
24". Summer visitor and passage migrant*. Adult plumage unmistakable. Immatures are distinguished from the larger Bittern by pale tips to wing feathers which form three broken wing bars. Usually only seen when feeding in the early morning or late afternoon. During the day roosts in trees or mangroves, sometimes in considerable numbers during migration. A few pairs have bred at Yim Tso Ha in recent years.

[BITTERN *Botaurus stellaris* 水駱駝
not illustrated
30". Winter visitor (November to April). Similar to immature Night Heron but larger with black cap and moustache stripe. Secretive and usually only seen when flushed from thick cover. A few birds are seen annually on the Deep Bay Marshes. DB]

LITTLE EGRET   breeding

CATTLE EGRET
breeding

non-breeding

CATTLE EGRET

CHINESE POND HERON
breeding

SWINHOE'S EGRET
breeding

non-breeding

GREAT EGRET
breeding

immature

non-breeding

NIGHT HERON
adult

Karen Phillipps

SOLITARY HERONS AND BITTERNS

YELLOW BITTERN *Ixobrychus sinensis* 小水駱駝
15". Summer visitor.* Distinctive black and fawn appearance in flight. Immatures are heavily streaked but the basic wing pattern is still clearly seen. Often perch on top of mangroves and reeds. Common on the Deep Bay Marshes from April until October but odd birds are seen there throughout the winter. Only occasionally seen elsewhere. An estimated 20 to 50 pairs breed each year with a possible recent increase due to the spread of coastal mangrove in Deep Bay. The nest is constructed of reeds near the ground.
≋ 🦆 DB

LITTLE GREEN HERON *Butorides striatus* 綠鷺
18". Local resident.* Slate grey in flight often with conspicuous orange soles to feet. Immatures are browner and have heavily streaked underparts. Invariably raises crest on alighting. Nearly always solitary and is more active at dawn and dusk. Mostly recorded in summer and autumn on the Mai Po Marshes but occurs, often throughout the year, wherever coastal mangrove is found. In winter occasionally seen along upland streams such as the headwaters to Tai Lam Chung Reservoir. Breeding has been proved and is considered to breed regularly at Deep Bay and in the Sai Kung area.
≋ 🦆

CHESTNUT BITTERN *Ixobrychus cinnamomeus* 栗葦鳽
15". Summer visitor (April to September). Uniform bright cinnamon-red wings and tail of male are diagnostic. Females are duller and immatures are browner, barred and spotted with buff. When flushed flies in a straight line with legs trailing. Regular on the Deep Bay Marshes but also occasionally elsewhere. Breeding has not been proved.
≋ 🦆 DB

REEF EGRET *Egretta sacra* 岩鷺
23". Local resident.* Distinctive grey appearance although a rare white form and even pied birds are occasionally reported. Confined to rocky coasts. Breeds on remote offshore islands. The nest is constructed of sticks amongst rocks near the tideline.
🦆

BLACK BITTERN *Dupetor flavicollis* 黑鳽
24". Occasional summer visitor (April to September). Very long neck held in a half extended 'S' in flight distinguishes it from Little Green Heron. Females are duller brownish-grey. Nocturnal and rarely seen although probably regular on the Deep Bay Marshes. Breeding has not been proved.
≋ 🦆 DB

YELLOW BITTERN adult

LITTLE GREEN HERON

CHESTNUT BITTERN

REEF EGRET

BLACK BITTERN

Karen Phillipps

CORMORANT, LARGE HERONS AND PELICANS

○ **CORMORANT** *Phalacrocorax carbo* 鸕鷀
33". Winter visitor (October to April). Large black seabird with long hook-tipped bill. White thigh patches are lost outside of the breeding season. Some older birds have almost the complete head and neck white. Immatures are dull brownish with mainly white underparts. Dives frequently and is often seen standing on rocks with wings hanging out to dry. Large flocks fly in lines. Coastal but also seen at Plover Cove and Tai Lam Chung Reservoirs. Particularly favours Deep Bay where flocks of up to 600 are regular. Much more common on the western side of Hong Kong. Sizeable roosts have been noted at Tree Island, Stonecutters' Island and Hei Ling Chau. Domesticated in Central and South China where they are largely bred in captivity and trained to catch fish.

○ **PURPLE HERON** *Ardea purpurea* 紫鷺
38". Non-breeding visitor. Distinctive and could only be confused with the larger Grey Heron; note predominantly reddish-brown appearance, thin neck and when flying comparative lack of contrast on the upperparts. Mostly seen in ones and twos and often only a distinctive snake-like head and neck is seen protruding above the mangroves. Occurs throughout the year on the Deep Bay Marshes but tends to be scarce in winter. Rarely recorded elsewhere. Breeding has not been proved but as good numbers are seen in summer it is suspected.
DB

○ **GREY HERON** *Ardea cinerea* 蒼鷺
40". Winter visitor (August to April). Distinctive pale grey and white appearance. Strongly contrasting upper wings in flight distinguishes it from Purple Heron. Most often seen in the Deep Bay area in winter, where roosting flocks of up to 200 are common. Odd birds are occasionally met with in summer. Only rarely seen elsewhere.
DB

PELICANS

Unmistakable, huge aquatic birds. Sexes are alike, but immatures are brownish. Gregarious, feed on fish— sometimes hunting in a co-ordinated effort with several individuals forming an ever-closing circle thereby driving the fish into the centre where they are easily caught. Flocks occur in Deep Bay every winter and are best seen with powerful binoculars or telescope from the road leading to Tsim Bei Tsui Police Post from Lau Fau Shan. Often, because of distance, it is not possible to identify the particular species but the colour of the pouch and underwing are important points to note.

○ **DALMATIAN PELICAN** *Pelecanus crispus* 捲羽鵜鶘
65". Winter visitor (December to April). Bright orange gular pouch (often yellowish in winter) and relatively small area of black on the underwing (tips of primaries only) separates this species from Spotted-Billed Pelican. Only recorded from Deep Bay. First identified in 1971, since when flocks of up to 80 have been seen in every winter.
DB

SPOTTED-BILLED PELICAN *Pelecanus philippensis* 斑嘴鵜鶘
55" Occasional winter visitor. Best separated from Dalmatian Pelican by the black wedge along the entire length of the underwing. Only recorded from Deep Bay.
DB

CORMORANT

PURPLE HERON adult

PURPLE HERON immature

GREY HERON

SPOTTED-BILLED PELICAN

DALMATIAN PELICAN

Karen Phillipps

STORKS, SPOONBILLS AND IBIS

Large, long-legged wading birds which fly with neck outstretched (a useful distinction from herons). Bill shape and colour are important aids to identification.

BLACK STORK *Ciconia nigra* 烏鶴
38". Occasional winter visitor (November to March). Distinctive glossy black and white appearance. Immatures have black parts browner, bill and legs yellowish. In flight its cruciform shape (the neck being the longest part) is noticeable at great distances. Usually occurs in small flocks, almost exclusively in the Deep Bay area where it is possibly regular. ≋ ⵣ DB

WHITE STORK *Ciconia ciconia boyciana* 白鶴
40". Vagrant. Distinctive white plumage with black wing feathers. Only two records of two over Clearwater Bay in March, 1961 and one on the Deep Bay Marshes during February 1967. The race which has occurred in Hong Kong is distinguished from the White Stork of Europe by its black, not red, bill. This subspecies is listed in the Red Data Book of Endangered Species of the International Union for the Conservation of Nature and Natural Resources. DB ⵣ

SPOONBILLS
The highly specialised bill is unique to spoonbills and when feeding is immersed in water and swept from side to side. Usually occur in flocks, which fly in lines, but odd birds are occasionally met with in flocks of egrets. Immatures have some grey and black in the primaries. All records are confined to the Deep Bay area.

BLACK-FACED SPOONBILL (LESSER SPOONBILL) *Platalea minor* 黑臉琵鷺
30". Winter visitor (August to May). Separated from European Spoonbill by its entirely blackish-grey bill and black facial skin. Usually seen in small flocks of up to 30, mostly in spring and autumn. ≋ ⵣ DB

EUROPEAN SPOONBILL *Platalea leucorodia* 琵鷺
33". Winter visitor (September to April). Separated from Black-Faced Spoonbill by the yellow tip to its bill and yellowish facial skin. First identified on 31 March, 1975, but has subsequently been regularly recorded and was most likely previously overlooked. ≋ ⵣ DB

WHITE IBIS *Threskiornis melanocephalus* 白鶃
30". Non-breeding visitor. Distinctive long decurved bill, unfeathered black head and neck. Immatures are greyer. Regularly recorded on the Deep Bay Marshes in flocks of up to 25 between November and March, but occasionally seen in summer. There is no evidence of breeding, but in June, 1974 three adults showed a distinct interest in the now destroyed egretry at Au Tau. ≋ ⵣ DB

[CRANE *Grus grus* 灰鶴 (蕃薯鶴)
not illustrated
45". Occasional visitor (November and December). Huge grey bird with distinctive black and white head and neck with scarlet patch on crown. Dark wing feathers droop over tail when standing. Recorded in parties of up to ten on the Deep Bay Marshes on six occasions. ≋ ⵣ DB]

Black Stork

BLACK STORK

WHITE STORK

BLACK-FACED
SPOONBILL

WHITE IBIS

EUROPEAN SPOONBILL

Karen Phillipps

SMALLER DABBLING DUCKS AND GREBES

DABBLING DUCKS

Feed on the surface or by up-ending, rarely dive. The brightly coloured speculum seen in flight is an important characteristic for identification. Females are much drabber and generally brown. Males adopt an eclipse plumage in autumn and resemble females.

TEAL *Anas crecca* 綠翼鴨
15". Winter visitor (August to April). Male distinctive. Females and eclipse males are difficult to separate from similar Garganey. With Garganey the smallest duck occurring in Hong Kong. Usually in flocks which fly fast and keep in tight formation. Takes off almost vertically. Very common in the Deep Bay area where several thousand are present in some winters, but also found on reservoirs and occasionally larger fish-ponds.

GARGANEY *Anas querquedula* 白眉鴨
16". Passage migrant (March to May and August to November). The prominent eyebrow and blue-grey forewing readily separate the male from similar Teal. The eyebrow is less prominent on the female but is still the best distinction from Teal. Fast flying. Occurs mainly on the Deep Bay Marshes where it is common on passage. Occasionally odd birds are seen at other times. DB

WIGEON *Anas penelope* 赤鴉鴨
19". Winter visitor (September to April). Chestnut head and white shoulders of the male are distinctive. A compact looking duck which flies in tight flocks. Regular in the Deep Bay area. DB

GREBES

Dive readily. Reluctant to fly, preferring to swim away. Head held low in flight. Sexes similar. Although, superficially resembling ducks they are not closely related.

GREAT CRESTED GREBE *Podiceps cristatus* 鳳頭鴉鴨
19". Winter visitor (November to April). Usually seen in winter plumage. In summer has distinctive chestnut and black frill around base of head and dark double-horned crest. The white cheeks and neck held erect are the best points for identification in Hong Kong. In flight, shows two conspicuous white patches on wings. Particularly favours Deep Bay where it is regular in small numbers, but is occasionally seen elsewhere along the coast and on the larger reservoirs. DB

LITTLE GREBE *Podiceps ruficollis* 水葫蘆
10". Local resident.* Smallest duck-like swimming bird seen in Hong Kong. Compact appearance. Prefers fresh water. Song is a whinnying trill and the alarm note is a sharp 'whit' 'whit'. A few pairs breed on the Mai Po Marshes and possibly on the larger reservoirs. The nest is built of floating vegetation.

Teal

Wigeon

♀

GARGANEY

♂

♀

TEAL

♂

♂

WIGEON

♀

LITTLE GREBE

winter

summer

GREAT CRESTED GREBE   winter

Karen Phillips

LARGE DUCKS

SHOVELER *Anas clypeata* 琵嘴鴨
20". Winter visitor (October to April). Both sexes are identified by the heavy spoon-shaped bill. When at rest or swimming sits low in the water with bill pointing downwards. Flocks of up to 100 are quite regular in the Deep Bay area.
≋ ⌇ DB

YELLOW-NIB DUCK *Anas poecilorhyncha* 斑嘴鴨
24". Non-breeding visitor. Large nondescript duck with pale head and neck. Commonest large duck on the Deep Bay Marshes with flocks of up to 100 in autumn and smaller numbers at other times. Occasionally seen elsewhere. May have bred prior to 1958. Breeds throughout China. Often seen for sale in Hong Kong markets.
≋ ⌇ DB

PINTAIL *Anas acuta* 針尾鴨
22"+4" (for tail of drake). Winter visitor (October to February). Male distinctive. Slender, long-necked appearance and pointed tail in flight. Flight is fast and direct with rapid wingbeats. Often up-ends when on water. Regular in the Deep Bay area where flocks of up to 100 are seen. Rarely recorded elsewhere.
≋ ⌇ DB

RED-BREASTED MERGANSER *Mergus serrator* 紅胸秋沙鴨
23". Winter visitor (December to April). Distinctive crest and bill. Sits low in the water. An accomplished diver and is usually submerged for 20 to 30 seconds. Regular in Deep Bay in small numbers and occasionally elsewhere around the coast.
⌇ DB

SHELDUCK *Tadorna tadorna* 冠鴨
24". Winter visitor (December to April). Unmistakable. Sexes are alike except that the drake has a knob above the bill in summer. Largest duck occurring in Hong Kong. Regular in the Deep Bay area in flocks of up to 450. Feeds on small molluscs which live just under the surface of the mud.
≋ ⌇ DB

Shoveler

Pintail

Yellow-nib Duck

YELLOW-NIB DUCK

SHOVELER

♂

♀

♀

PINTAIL

♂

♀

RED-BREASTED MERGANSER

♂

SHELDUCK

Karen Phillips.

RARER DUCKS

GADWALL *Anas strepera* 紫膀鴨
20″. Winter visitor (September to March). In flight all plumages have large white speculum which is diagnostic. Females are mottled brown and at rest are difficult to separate from similar female ducks. Recorded almost annually in very small numbers in the Deep Bay area. 〜 DB

FALCATED TEAL *Anas falcata* 羅紋鴨
19″. Winter visitor (September to April). In flight note dark green speculum (black in female), white wing bar and white collar. Head looks large, huge when crest is raised. Female is mottled brown. Several hundred winter in Deep Bay but records are sparse because these ducks are rarely seen over the main marsh. DB

BAER'S POCHARD *Aythya baeri* 青頭鴨
16″. Vagrant. Male separated from similar ducks by chestnut breast. Female is duller but has the same general pattern. Both sexes have a conspicuous white patch below tail and show a curved white wing bar in flight. There have been several winter records of one or two birds in the Deep Bay area in recent years. Possibly confused with Tufted Duck in the past. 〜 DB

TUFTED DUCK *Aythya fuligula* 鳳頭鴨
17″. Winter visitor (November to February). Rudimentary crest on the back of the head should separate this species from Baer's Pochard in all plumages. Broad white wing bar in flight. Female sometimes has a small white patch at the base of the bill and occasionally white under the tail but this is never as conspicuous as in Baer's Pochard. Dives frequently and normally keeps to fresh water. Quite regular in small numbers on the Deep Bay Marshes in recent years and once at Plover Cove Reservoir. 〜 DB

[**SCAUP** *Aythya marila* 斑背鴨
not illustrated
19″. Vagrant (December and January). Similar to respective plumages of Tufted Duck but lacks crest. Male separated by grey back and female by large white patch at the base of the bill. Broad white wing bar in flight. A sea duck in winter. Large flocks were seen in Tolo Harbour early this century and occasionally thereafter from widespread areas but has not been recorded since 1969.]

MALLARD *Anas platyrhynchos* 綠頭鴨
23″. Winter visitor (October to April). In flight both sexes show violet blue speculum between two white wing bars. Females and eclipse males are brown and difficult to separate from Yellow-nib Duck. Regular in very small numbers in the Deep Bay area, previously more widespread. 〜 DB

BEAN GOOSE *Anser fabalis* 大雁
32″. Vagrant. All grey geese are alike in the field. This species is separated by its dark head and neck (which look black at a distance), uniform dark wings in flight, black and yellow bill, orange legs and feet. Grey geese are probably annual winter visitors but are usually seen at too great a distance to permit specific identification. Two recent records from Kai Tak and Mai Po.

[**GREY-LAG GOOSE** *Anser anser* 灰雁
not illustrated
33″. Vagrant. (November and March). Separated with difficulty from other grey geese by pink bill and legs and pale grey forewing. Four records in the past twenty years, all from the Deep Bay area.]

Bean Geese

GADWALL

FALCATED TEAL

TUFTED DUCK

♀

BAER'S POCHARD

♂

MALLARD

Karen Phillipps

RAILS AND JACANA

RAILS

Shy birds frequenting marshland, paddy and margins of streams and ponds. Short tails and rounded wings with legs dangling in flight. Walk well but with distinctive head jerk and tail twitch. Run for nearest cover when disturbed. Young are invariably black and downy, leaving the nest after hatching.

WATERCOCK *Gallicrex cinerea* 董雞

17″. Summer and autumn visitor (April to November). Male has distinctive red frontal shield. Non-breeding males resemble females. Upright stance. In flight the neck and legs are outstretched. Regular on the Deep Bay Marshes and occasionally seen elsewhere. Breeding has not been proved but it is likely that several pairs bred annually between 1966 and 1974, however, recent destruction of its favoured habitat has resulted in this species becoming scarcer.

≋ DB

WHITE-BREASTED WATERHEN *Amaurornis phoenicurus* 白面雞

13″. Resident.* Distinctive plumage with bright chestnut vent. Noisy with a monotonous 'kee-wak' 'kee-wak' which can be kept up for considerable periods––even at night. Less secretive than most rails. Notably aggressive. Fairly numerous and widespread in the New Territories but local on Hong Kong Island. The breeding season commences as early as February and continues through to late summer. Nests are constructed in bushes, usually three to eight feet off the ground, not far from water. Clutches vary but generally four to six eggs are laid

≋ ◣

PHEASANT-TAILED JACANA *Hydrophasianus chirurgus* 水雉

12″+10″ (tail of breeding adult). Summer visitor* (May to October). Unmistakable. The elongated tail is lost in winter. Immatures resemble non-breeding birds but yellow neck patch is absent. Wings are mostly white in flight. Extremely long toes enable jacanas to walk on floating vegetation. Very scarce but regular visitor to the Deep Bay Marshes where a few pairs have bred annually since 1968, but destruction of its favoured habitat has led to a recent decline. Rarely seen elsewhere. Odd birds occasionally turn up in the winter months. The breeding season is from May to August and the nest is either floating, attached to reeds, or on marshy ground. Four eggs are laid. The female is larger than the male and the normal roles at the nest are reversed.

≋ DB

BANDED RAIL (SLATY-BREASTED RAIL) *Rallus striatus* 灰胸秧雞

10″. Local resident.* Distinctive chestnut crown and narrow white barring of upperparts on adults. Immatures are generally duller. Secretive and difficult to observe except at dawn and dusk. Widespread, occurring in small numbers throughout the New Territories, but most often seen on the Mai Po Marshes. Breeding has only recently been proved. The nest is a platform of grass or reeds placed on the ground or slightly elevated and attached to stems. Three or four young are usually reared.

≋

MOORHEN *Gallinula chloropus* 黑水雞

13″. Local resident.* White streak across flanks and white under tail-coverts are diagnostic. Immatures are browner. Jerky swimming action. Mainly recorded on the Deep Bay Marshes where it is not scarce, but also occurs in smaller numbers elsewhere. The breeding season extends from April to September. The nest is constructed of sticks and reeds close to water.

≋

COOT *Fulica atra* 白骨頂

16″. Non-breeding visitor. Distinctive white frontal shield. Gregarious. Swims in open water and dives well. When taking off runs along the surface of the water. Unusual lobed toes. Often abundant in the Deep Bay area in winter but numbers vary from year to year. A few are seen elsewhere. In recent years odd birds have been recorded in summer at Mai Po and, although suspected, breeding has not been proved.

≋

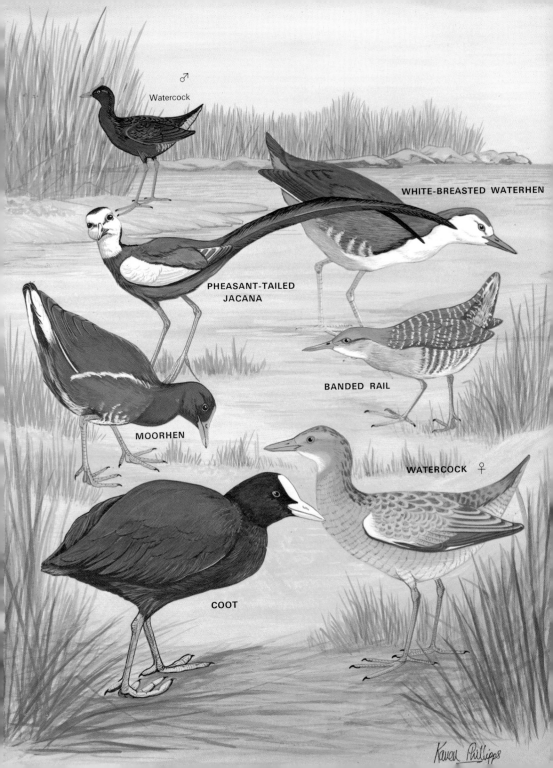

Watercock ♂

WHITE-BREASTED WATERHEN

PHEASANT-TAILED
JACANA

BANDED RAIL

MOORHEN

WATERCOCK ♀

COOT

Karen Phillipps

UNCOMMON RAILS AND SMALLER DUCKS

PAINTED SNIPE *Rostratula benghalensis* 彩鷸
10". Winter visitor (September to March). Distinctive. Male is a bleached version of the female. Difficult to flush. Rises from the ground heavily with legs trailing like a rail. Often several in a small area. Mostly active at dawn and dusk. Found in swampy areas and paddy-fields. Mainly recorded from the Deep Bay area and Long Valley but has become much scarcer in recent years. The name is a misnomer as this species is not a snipe.

CRIMSON-LEGGED CRAKE *Amaurornis akool* 紅脚苦惡鳥
10". Status uncertain.* Note lack of barring on underparts. Found in swampy areas and by small streams in paddy-fields. Breeding has been recorded in several recent years at Tsing Lung Tau and earlier suspected at Shek Kong but otherwise records have been very few. Possibly a regular summer visitor in small numbers. Nests in thick grass and reeds, usually in April.

RUDDY CRAKE *Porzana fusca* 紅胸田鷄
8½". Passage migrant (April to June, September and October). Note small size. Immatures are dark brown with whitish throat and centre of belly. Very shy. Most active at dawn and dusk. Scarce, but probably regular in small numbers. Mainly seen in the Deep Bay area. Has bred at Macau. ≋ DB

WATER RAIL *Rallus aquaticus* 秧鷄
12½". Winter visitor (September to April). Separated from crakes by long bill and from Banded Rail by streaked upperparts. Very shy and difficult to flush. Most active at dawn and dusk. Regular in small numbers, mainly in the Deep Bay area. ≋ DB

LESSER TREEDUCK (WHISTLING TEAL) *Dendrocygna javanica* 樹鴨
16". Occasional visitor (April to October). Looks like a small goose. In flight, appears generally dark with no conspicuous markings but note head carried lower than body and rounded wings. Recorded on a few occasions in parties of up to eleven, mainly in the Deep Bay area where it may have bred in 1968 and 1969. ≋ DB

COTTON TEAL *Nettapus coromandelianus* 棉鳧
13". Vagrant (September and October). Small size and black and white appearance of male is diagnostic. Female is similar but black parts replaced by brown and lacks collar. Broad white wing patches seen in flight. Four records from the Deep Bay area since 1969.

PAINTED SNIPE

CRIMSON-LEGGED CRAKE

WATER RAIL

RUDDY CRAKE

COTTON TEAL

LESSER TREEDUCK

SHOREBIRDS

PLOVERS

Plump, thick-necked, short-billed shorebirds. Gregarious. Fly strongly, often in compact flocks. Run swiftly and when feeding they typically run a short distance, stop and hold their heads as if listening. Found on sandy shores, exposed mud and occasionally bare ground and grassy areas but invariably near water. Sexes are usually alike.

KENTISH PLOVER *Charadrius alexandrinus* 鴴 (白鴴)
6''. Non-breeding visitor. The adult male has an incomplete black breast band and rufous crown. In winter the crown is brown. Females and immatures resemble winter males but the patches on the sides of the breast are brown. Separated in all plumages from Little Ringed Plover by dark legs and white wing bar. Although recorded throughout the year most records fall between August and May. Common in the Deep Bay area, where flocks of up to 500 have been seen, but also found elsewhere in much smaller numbers and usually on sandy beaches.

LITTLE RINGED PLOVER *Charadrius dubius* 黑領鴴
7''. Non-breeding visitor. Summer birds have a complete black gorget. Immatures have the black markings replaced by brown and the gorget is sometimes incomplete. Separated from Kentish Plover in all plumages by lack of wing bar and yellowish legs. Although recorded throughout the year most records fall between September and April. Usually only seen in small parties but flocks of up to 200 occur on passage. Common in the Deep Bay area but also regularly seen elsewhere, usually along the shore, in winter.

GREY PLOVER *Pluvialis squatarola* 灰斑鴴
11''. Winter visitor (September to April). Can only be confused with Asiatic Golden Plover, but is separated in all plumages by its black axillaries (armpits) seen in flight. In summer the underparts are black and the upperparts strikingly black and white. Triple call note 'tee-oo-ee' is not unlike a wolf whistle. Mostly seen on the Deep Bay Marshes in small flocks of up to 74, but odd birds are occasionally seen elsewhere along the shore.

GREATER SAND-PLOVER *Charadrius leschenaultii* 鐵嘴沙鴴
9''. Non-breeding visitor. Lack of white collar identifies sand-plovers from Kentish and Little Ringed Plovers in all plumages. Difficult to separate from smaller Mongolian Sand-Plover but has a larger bill and narrower breast band in summer. Mostly seen in the Deep Bay area where large flocks of up to 200 can be seen in April, September and October. Elsewhere, small parties can occasionally be met with along the shore; usually in winter.

[MONGOLIAN SAND-PLOVER *Charadrius mongolus* 蒙古沙鴴
not illustrated
8''. Passage migrant (April to June and August to October). Only separated from Greater Sand-Plover with difficulty, but has a smaller and shorter bill and a broader breast band in summer. Much less common than Greater Sand-Plover, only occurring in small numbers but quite often in the same localities. DB]

[ORIENTAL PLOVER *Charadrius veredus* 紅胸鴴
not illustrated
9''. Passage migrant (March to May, September and October). Similar to sand-plovers but the entire breast is grey-brown in winter and chestnut narrowly bordered below with a black band in summer. Very scarce; in recent years the few records have been confined to the restricted area of Kai Tak Airport.]

TURNSTONE *Arenaria interpres* 翻石鷸
9''. Passage migrant (April, May, August and September). Striking pied wing pattern and short orange legs. In winter the plumage is more mottled and has a messy appearance. Feeds by turning over pebbles to expose small animals, hence its name. Mostly seen in the Deep Bay area in small flocks of up to 30 but is occasionally seen elsewhere along the shore. DB

Kentish Plover

Little Ringed Plover

Grey Plover
winter

GREY PLOVER

KENTISH PLOVER

GREATER SAND-PLOVER
summer

TURNSTONE   summer

GREATER SAND-PLOVER
winter

LITTLE RINGED PLOVER
summer

Karen Phillips

SHOREBIRDS

LAPWING *Vanellus vanellus* 鳳頭麥雞
12''. Winter visitor (November to February). Distinctive. In summer the throat is black. Scarce but regular, usually commoner during a hard winter. Flocks of up to 35 have been seen, principally in the Deep Bay area and Long Valley but quite often elsewhere. ♣♣ ≈

GREY-HEADED LAPWING *Vanellus cinereus* 灰頭麥雞
14''. Winter visitor (September to April). Distinctive. In flight shows large white area on inner wing, black primaries and grey forewing. A flock of up to 20 regularly winters in Long Valley. Elsewhere, usually seen on migration particularly in the Deep Bay area but can turn up anywhere. In October, 1976, a flock of some 20 birds descended on Happy Valley Racecourse during an evening meeting. ♣♣ ≈

ASIATIC GOLDEN PLOVER *Pluvialis dominicus* 金錢鴴
10''. Non-breeding visitor. Appears heavy-bodied with big head. In flight the upperparts are uniform brownish. Breeding birds are black below and the upperparts mottled black and gold with a conspicuous white eyebrow continuing down the sides of the breast. Regular in the Deep Bay area in parties of up to 50. Odd birds are occasionally seen elsewhere. Recorded in all months except July. ♣♣ ≈

BAR-TAILED GODWIT *Limosa lapponica* 斑尾鷸
15''. Passage migrant. (April, May and September to December). Separated from Black-Tailed Godwit by shorter more upturned bill, lack of wing bar in flight and narrowly barred tail. Distinguished fom Asian Dowitcher by two-toned bill. In winter, the plumage is greyer, generally similar to Asian Dowitcher. Virtually confined to the Deep Bay Marshes where it is scarce but regular in small flocks. ≈ ⌐ DB

ASIAN DOWITCHER *Limnodromus semipalmatus* 半蹼鷸
14''. Passage migrant (April, May and August, September). Separated from similar Bar-Tailed Godwit by straight all black bill, shorter legs which do not project beyond tail in flight and unusual rapid stabbing style of feeding when the bill is often buried to the hilt. In summer, the plumage is rufous, generally similar to Bar-Tailed Godwit. Flocks of up to 26 have been recorded on the Deep Bay Marshes in recent years. This species is listed in the Red Data Book of Endangered Species of the International Union for the Conservation of Nature and Natural Resources. Hong Kong is probably the best place in the world to see this extremely rare bird. ≈ DB

RUFF (REEVE) *Philomachus pugnax* 流蘇鷸
12'' (male), 9–11'' (female). Passage migrant (March, April and September to December). In flight shows diagnostic white oval patches on either side of the upper tail. Female (reeve) is similar to the winter male. Plumage including leg colour is variable, but note scaly appearance of back. In summer, the male develops an extraordinary multi-coloured ruff but to date this has never been recorded in Hong Kong. ≈ DB

LAPWING winter

GREY-HEADED LAPWING

ASIATIC GOLDEN PLOVER winter

summer

BAR-TAILED GODWIT

winter
ASIAN DOWITCHER

RUFF winter

Karen Phillipps

LARGE SHOREBIRDS

WHIMBREL *Numenius phaeopus* 中杓鷸
17″. Passage migrant (April to June and August to October). Shorter bill, broadly striped crown and quicker wingbeats separate this species from the larger Curlew. Has a distinctive call which is an even tittering trill of seven whistling notes. Often seen in flocks of up to 100. Mostly recorded in the Deep Bay area, but is regularly seen elsewhere—particularly in Tolo Harbour and Mirs Bay.

[**LITTLE WHIMBREL** *Numenius minutus* 小杓鷸
not illustrated.
12″. Occasional visitor (May and October). Like a miniature Whimbrel but with rump, upper tail-coverts and tail the same colour as the mantle. Very scarce; virtually all records are confined to the restricted area of Kai Tak Airport.

BLACK-TAILED GODWIT *Limosa limosa* 黑尾鷸
16″. Winter visitor (August to May). Distinctive flight pattern. In summer plumage resembles Bar-Tailed Godwit but throat is whitish, belly and under tail-coverts dusky white only tinged rufous and breast and belly have broad dark bars. Legs trail well behind tail in flight. Only recorded from the Deep Bay Marshes, where flocks of up to 50 are regular.

CURLEW *Numenius arquata* 白腰杓鷸
23″. Winter visitor (August to May). Larger and with an even longer bill than Whimbrel. In flight, has a prominent white rump and lower back forming a white triangle. Flight is strong with a measured beat and flocks fly high in lines or chevrons. The call is a distinctive loud musical 'cour li' rising in pitch. Regular, in small numbers, in the Deep Bay area but flocks of up to 100 have occasionally been seen.

[**AUSTRALIAN CURLEW** *Numenius madagascariensis* 大杓鷸
not illustrated
23″. Passage migrant (April, May, September and October). Similar to Curlew but lower back, rump and tail are the same colour as the mantle. Very scarce, being mainly seen on the Deep Bay Marshes in small numbers in spring.

AVOCET *Recurvirostra avosetta* 反嘴鷸
17″. Winter visitor (November to February). Unmistakable. Feeds with a side to side sifting motion of the head. Only recorded from the Deep Bay area, in flocks of up to 50, where it is scarce but probably regular.

BLACK-WINGED STILT *Himantopus himantopus* 黑翅長腳鷸
15″. Passage migrant (April, May and August to December). Distinctive appearance, note the extraordinary long legs. The extent of shading on the head and neck is variable. Immatures are brownish. Regular on the Deep Bay Marshes, where up to 20 are recorded annually. Has occasionally been seen elsewhere along the coast.

Whimbrel

Black-Tailed Godwit

winter
BLACK-TAILED GODWIT

WHIMBREL

CURLEW

AVOCET

BLACK-WINGED STILT

SHOREBIRDS

GREEN SANDPIPER *Tringa ochropus* 白腰泥岸鷸
9½". Non-breeding visitor. Separated from other sandpipers by blackish underwing, prominent white rump contrasting with dark upperparts and dark legs. No wing bar. When flushed rises with a loud shrill 'weet-a-weet', zigzagging at first then climbing high, circles and finally drops steeply to alight on the ground some distance away. Usually seen singly or in small parties. Feeds on banks of streams, fish-ponds and flooded fields, but rarely if ever along the shore. Fairly widespread throughout the New Territories and is almost always seen between August and May.

COMMON SANDPIPER *Actitis hypoleucos* 磯鷸
8". Non-breeding visitor. Distinguished by broad white wing bar and distinctive flight low over water. In flight the wings are flicked downwards (often almost touching the water) between glides. Bobs head and tail constantly. Perches on low objects. Call is shrill piping 'twee-wee-wee-wee.' Usually seen singly or in pairs but often many are found in a small area of suitable habitat. Occurs around the coast, by watercourses and along the banks of fish-ponds. Common and widespread, but mostly seen between August and May.

WOOD SANDPIPER *Tringa glareola* 林鷸
9". Non-breeding visitor. Separated from Green Sandpiper by pale underwing, less prominent white rump and pale legs which project beyong the tail in flight. No wing bar. Towers when flushed. Call is a loud rapid sharp shrill 'wee-wee-wee' or 'wit-wit-wit' in flight. Usually seen in flocks which may be several hundred strong in spring. Widespread in the New Territories being found in flooded areas but particularly favours marshland, fish-ponds (when drained) and the damp grazing areas either side of the Lok Ma Chau Road. Most records fall between August and May.

GREY-RUMPED SANDPIPER *Heteroscelus brevipes* 灰鷸
10". Passage migrant (April to November). Identified by unmarked dark grey upperparts. Call is a sharp double whistle 'too-weet.' Small flocks of up to 20 occur around the coast during both migrations, but occasionally a few are seen in midsummer.

RED-NECKED STINT (EASTERN LITTLE STINT) *Calidris ruficollis* 紅脖鷸
6½". Non-breeding visitor. Small size and short bill distinguish stints from other shorebirds. However, it is difficult to separate the individual species of stint, particularly in winter plumage. This species has black legs and black bill in all plumages and in summer is separated by its distinctly rufous upper breast, neck and sides of head. Mostly recorded from the Deep Bay area during migration when flocks of several hundred have been seen in April. Occasionally seen elsewhere along the shore in much smaller numbers.   DB

[**TEMMINCK'S STINT** *Calidris temminckii* 灰背鷸
not illustrated
6". Winter visitor (September to May). Yellowish or greenish legs. In winter plumage separated from other stints by uniform, darker and duller brownish grey upperparts. Towers when flushed. More of a marshland bird than a shorebird. Mostly recorded from the Deep Bay area in flocks of up to 40 and only rarely seen elsewhere.   DB]

RED-NECKED PHALAROPE *Phalaropus lobatus* 紅頸瓣蹼鷸
7½". Passage migrant (March to June and August to October). Black needle bill, slender appearance and habit of swimming identify this species. Broad white wing bar in flight. Females are brighter and somewhat larger than males. Swims buoyantly, high out of the water and often well out to sea. Spins rapidly and constantly moves head when feeding on water. Usually in flocks. Flight is graceful and swallow-like. Tame. Principally maritime but is also found inland on fish-ponds. Numbers vary greatly from year to year and in some years flocks of several hundred are seen, even in Victoria Harbour. There is some evidence to show that numbers increase after bad weather.

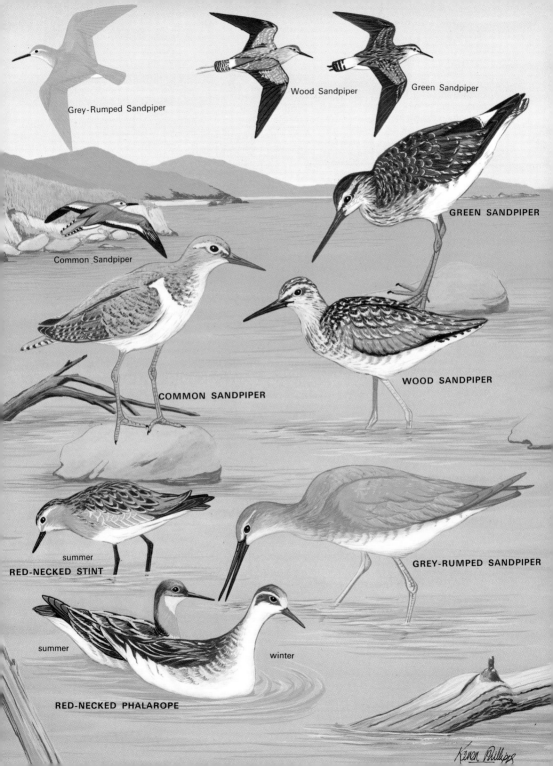

Grey-Rumped Sandpiper

Wood Sandpiper

Green Sandpiper

GREEN SANDPIPER

Common Sandpiper

COMMON SANDPIPER

WOOD SANDPIPER

summer

RED-NECKED STINT

GREY-RUMPED SANDPIPER

summer

winter

RED-NECKED PHALAROPE

Karen Phillipps

SHOREBIRDS

REDSHANK   *Tringa totanus*   赤足鷸
11". Non-breeding visitor. In flight shows distinctive broad white band on trailing edge of inner wing. At rest separated from similar shorebirds; except Spotted Redshank, by red or orange legs. Generally browner than Spotted Redshank. Noisy; loud musical 'teu-hu-hu' (first note higher in pitch). Quite shy and when alarmed bobs energetically then springs into the air uttering loud call notes. Principally a migrant and most birds are seen in April, May and August to October, usually in small flocks. Mostly recorded on the Deep Bay Marshes, but also quite regularly elsewhere.

GREENSHANK   *Tringa nebularia*   青脚鷸
14". Non-breeding visitor. Note large size, long, rather heavy, slightly upturned bill and broad white triangle extending up back contrasting with unmarked wings in flight. In winter, upperparts are grey and underparts white. Noisy; very loud ringing 'chew' 'chew' 'chew.' Usually in small parties but occasionally large flocks are seen. Mostly recorded in the Deep Bay area but also quite regularly elsewhere in small numbers. Not often seen in June and July.

SPOTTED REDSHANK   *Tringa erythropus*   赤足鶴鷸
12". Winter visitor (September to May). Separated from Redshank by lack of clear white band in wing (although shows indistinct mottled white bar) and longer bill. In winter much paler and greyer. Call is a loud sharp 'tewit' (rising at the end). Unlike most shorebirds quite readily swims. Confined to the Deep Bay area where it is common in winter. In spring flocks of up to 300 are recorded.   DB

MARSH SANDPIPER   *Tringa stagnatilis*   澤鷸
10". Passage migrant (February to May, August to December). Smaller and slenderer version of Greenshank. Very trim, needle-like bill. Long legs which trail well behind the tail in flight. In winter, plumage is paler and greyer. Very active. Regular in the Deep Bay area, where flocks of up to 50 are seen. Rarely recorded elsewhere.   DB

RED KNOT   *Calidris canutus*   紅腹鷸
10". Passage migrant (April to June and August to November). Short-legged and chunky. Dirty whitish rump. In winter, upperparts are grey with white eyebrow and underparts white with faint streaks. Forms very compact flocks. Virtually confined to the Deep Bay area where it is scarce but regular in small numbers.   DB

GREAT KNOT   *Calidris tenuirostris*   薄嘴鷸
12". Passage migrant (April, May and August to November). In winter, is greyer but usually has a blackish breast band of spots which separates it from Red Knot. Confined to the Deep Bay area where it is scarce but regular in small flocks.   DB

TEREK SANDPIPER   *Xenus cinereus*   翹嘴鷸
10". Passage migrant (March to June and August to November). Long upturned black bill with yellowish base and short orange legs are diagnostic. In flight shows broad white bar similar to Redshank. Frequently bobs. Winter plumage is greyer. Mostly recorded on the Deep Bay Marshes where flocks of up to 60 are seen in spring and up to 25 in autumn. Quite regularly occurs elsewhere in smaller numbers.

Redshank

GREENSHANK summer

SPOTTED REDSHANK summer

RED KNOT summer

MARSH SANDPIPER summer

GREAT KNOT summer

TEREK SANDPIPER summer

Karen Phillipps

SMALLER SHOREBIRDS

SHARP-TAILED SANDPIPER *Calidris acuminata* 尖尾鷸
$8\frac{1}{2}$". Passage migrant (April, May and August to October). Separated from Wood Sandpiper and Ruff by rufous crown and bold black streaks on upperparts. Larger than stints. In flight, note thin white wing bar and whitish sides to tail and rump. In winter, plumage is less rufous and the underparts less spotted. Regular on the Deep Bay Marshes in small numbers and occasionally elsewhere.

[LONG-TOED STINT *Calidris subminuta* 長趾鷸
not illustrated
$6\frac{1}{4}$". Winter visitor (September to May). A smaller version of the Sharp-Tailed Sandpiper. Separated from Temminck's Stint by bold black streaks on brownish upperparts and from Red-Necked Stint by pale legs. Regular on the Deep Bay Marshes, particularly at Lok Ma Chau. Occasionally seen elsewhere. ≋ DB]

CURLEW SANDPIPER *Calidris ferruginea* 彎嘴鷸
$8\frac{1}{2}$". Passage migrant (March to May and July to November). Separated from Dunlin and Broad-Billed Sandpiper by white rump and longer legs and from Red Knot by long decurved bill. In winter plumage the upperparts are plain grey with white eyebrow and the underparts whitish with a greyish or buffish wash to the breast. Common on the Deep Bay Marshes in spring when flocks of up to 300 are seen with many birds in full breeding plumage. Much scarcer in autumn. Occasionally seen elsewhere. ≋ DB

BROAD-BILLED SANDPIPER *Limicola falcinellus* 濶嘴鷸
7". Passage migrant (March to June and August to November). Separated from stints by larger size and longer bill, slightly decurved at tip. In winter, the upperparts are greyer and less well marked. Appears very dark in flight showing no wing bar. Regular on the Deep Bay Marshes, usually only a few together but flocks of up to 45 occur. Occasionally seen elsewhere. ≋ DB

SPOON-BILLED SANDPIPER *Eurynorhynchus pygmeus* 匙嘴鷸
6". Passage migrant (March to May, September and October). Unique spatulate bill, but is often difficult to see. In winter the upperparts are pale greyish with clear white forehead. Regular, mostly in spring, but usually only one or two seen each year. Records are confined to the Deep Bay Marshes. ≋ DB

DUNLIN *Calidris alpina* 黑腹鷸
$7\frac{1}{2}$". Winter visitor (August to May). Separated from Sharp-Tailed Sandpiper, Sanderling and Ruff by long, slightly decurved bill. In winter separated from Curlew Sandpiper by broad black line down centre of rump and tail. Winter plumage is greyer and lacks black waistcoat on the underparts. Regularly recorded from the Deep Bay area where flocks of several hundred are sometimes seen. Occasionally occurs elsewhere but usually only odd birds. ≋ DB

SANDERLING *Crocethia alba* 三趾鷸
8". Passage migrant. (April to June and July to November). In flight, shows broad white wing bar and black shoulder patch. In summer, the upperparts, sides of head, neck and upper breast are mottled rufous and black contrasting with the white abdomen. Prefers to run rather than fly when approached. Regular on passage to the Deep Bay area where flocks of over 200 have been seen in spring. Occasionally odd birds are seen elsewhere. Records suggest that it has become scarcer in recent years. ≋

SHARP-TAILED SANDPIPER
summer

CURLEW SANDPIPER
summer

summer

BROAD-BILLED
SANDPIPER

SPOON-BILLED SANDPIPER
summer

SANDERLING   winter

DUNLIN   summer

PRATINCOLE, SNIPE, FRANCOLIN AND QUAIL

ORIENTAL PRATINCOLE *Glareola maldivarum* 燕鴴
10″. Non-breeding visitor. Distinctive. Prominent white rump. Underwing blackish with chestnut lining. Swallow-like in flight with long pointed wings and deeply forked tail. Immatures lack black throat border and breast is mottled rufous white. Regular in small numbers but flocks of up to 150 recorded. Usually seen on migration in widespread areas but favouring level coastal sites. Juveniles have been seen at Kai Tak in midsummer in recent years.

SNIPE
Distinctive medium-sized brown wetland birds with long bills and short legs. Specific identification of each species in the field is difficult even for experts. Usually stay under cover in dense vegetation until flushed but occasionally seen feeding in the open. Small parties (known as 'wisps') form aerial evolutions.

FANTAIL SNIPE (COMMON SNIPE) *Gallinago gallinago* 扇尾鷸
11″. Winter visitor (August to May). In flight, separated from other snipe by narrow but conspicuous white trailing edge to secondaries. When flushed emits a loud 'creech' call followed by a highly erratic flight. This is our commonest snipe, found in most marshy areas, but particularly favours Lok Ma Chau and the Mai Po Marshes. At Lok Ma Chau good numbers can often be seen feeding in the open close to the road.

[PINTAIL SNIPE *Gallinago stenura* 針尾鷸
not illustrated
10″. Winter visitor (August to April). Lacks white trailing edge to secondaries. Call is a nasal "squak" when flushed, which should separate this species from Swinhoe's Snipe. Can be identified with certainty in the hand by extemely narrow outer tail feathers. Prefers drier areas than Fantail Snipe. Much less common, although widespread.

[SWINHOE'S SNIPE *Gallinago megala* 大沙鷸
not illustrated
11″. Passage migrant (August to April). Virtually indistinguishable in the field from Pintail Snipe but some hunters claim to recognise its larger size and heavier flight. In the hand is identified by its 20 tail feathers. Much scarcer than either Fantail or Pintail Snipe although its exact status is unknown. Apparently absent during midwinter.

WOODCOCK *Scolopax rusticola* 丘鷸
14″. Winter visitor (August to April). Distinguished from snipe by larger size, triangular head shape, barred crown and broad round wings. Usually only seen when flushed from cover but sometimes seen flying at dawn and dusk when flight appears owlish. Feeds at night and spends the day at rest in bamboo thickets, hedges or woodland margins often quite close to villages. Widespread in the New Territories, but in recent years has become quite scarce.

JAPANESE QUAIL *Coturnix japonica* 鵪鶉
7½″. Winter visitor (September to April). A small, round, very short-tailed bird of grassy hillsides which suddenly flushes from underfoot. Prominent eyebrow separates this species from button-quails. Females are more heavily streaked than males. Skulks. Widespread in the New Territories, numbers vary from year to year but is becoming scarcer. Used to be heavily netted in China. Reared in captivity in Hong Kong for their eggs which are laid throughout the year.

CHINESE FRANCOLIN *Francolinus pintadeanus* 鷓鴣
13″. Resident.* Females and immatures are generally browner. Loud grating call, "come to the Peak, ha-ha" (Herklots). Heard much more often than seen. Runs fast and is difficult to flush. Quite common and widespread, found on grass covered hills or in open pine woods. Best seen in spring when it calls in the open, usually perched on rocks. Feeds at dawn and dusk. Pairing occurs in March and April when a simple nest of grass, dry leaves and a few feathers is constructed, well hidden, on the ground. Four or five eggs are laid and there are usually two broods. Sold in large numbers in Hong Kong markets.

BARRED BUTTON-QUAIL *Turnix suscitator* 棕三趾鶉
6½″. Winter visitor (October to March). When flushed button-quails are similar to Japanese Quail. Two species have occurred, this species being separated from the Yellow-Legged Button-Quail by its black markings which are more apparent on females. Button-quails have been rarely recorded in recent years although they may be regular visitors to the grass covered hills of the remoter parts of the New Territories. Known as Mandarin Quails to local hunters.

ORIENTAL PRATINCOLE

FANTAIL SNIPE

JAPANESE QUAIL

WOODCOCK

CHINESE FRANCOLIN
♂

BARRED BUTTON-QUAIL
♀

Karen Phillipps

TERNS

Graceful sea and marshland birds with long, narrow, pointed wings and forked tails. Less robust and generally smaller than gulls. Sexes are alike. Rarely rest on the surface of the water.

WHITE-WINGED BLACK TERN *Chidonias leucoptera* 黑海燕
10". Passage migrant (April to June and August to November). Distinctive black head, body and wing linings in breeding plumage. Non-breeding birds are difficult to separate from similar Whiskered Terns but have a whitish not grey rump. Feeds by fluttering over water, scooping insects from the surface Rarely dives. Flocks of up to 100 are regular in spring, but less common in autumn. Usually seen in the Deep Bay area, but can occur anywhere around the coast.

WHISKERED TERN *Chlidonias hybrida* 鬚海燕
11" Non-breeding visitor. Distinctive white cheeks and wing linings in breeding plumage. Juveniles have a mottled brown mantle. Non-breeding birds are difficult to separate from similar White-Winged Black Terns but have a grey not whitish rump. Distinctive feeding method as for White-Winged Black Tern. Commoner in autumn, when flocks of up to 100 are recorded, but odd birds can be seen at almost any time. Mostly in the Deep Bay area but can occur anywhere around the coast.

COMMON TERN *Sterna hirundo* 普通海燕
13". Passage migrant (April to June and September). Difficult to separate from Arctic Tern (*Sterna paradisaea*) and Roseate Tern (*Sterna dougallii*) both of which could occur here. However, the extensive dark undersides to the wing-tips and in winter the extent of the dark forewings help to distinguish this species. Terns which could be attributable to any of these three species are seen annually in coastal waters during migration, most often in spring.

CASPIAN TERN *Sterna caspia* 紅嘴巨海燕
21". Non-breeding visitor. Identified by large size, stout red bill and blackish underside to primaries. Regular visitor to the Deep Bay area, throughout the year, but occasionally seen elsewhere. In winter many birds roost at Nim Wan near Lau Fau Shan, where up to 80 have been counted.

GULLS

Adults are mostly white with grey wings and mantle but this plumage is only acquired after several years of intermediate phases. Sexes are alike. Immatures usually have some brown in the plumage. Wings are long and broader than terns and the tail is not forked. Legs are sturdy, adapted for walking and swimming. Frequently rest on the sea, often in large flotillas. Strong direct flight but can also soar gracefully. Surface feeders, eating almost anything. Winter visitors to Hong Kong.

BLACK-HEADED GULL *Larus ridibundus* 紅嘴鷗
15". Winter visitor (October to April). Usually seen in winter plumage. Separated from other gulls by small size and long white wedge on the primaries in flight. Summer birds have chocolate brown heads and are occasionally seen here in spring. Immatures are like winter birds but have a black terminal band on the tail. Very common in coastal waters in winter, including Victoria Harbour, but tend to avoid more sheltered areas except in hard weather. Huge numbers visit Hong Kong and an estimated 6500 were roosting off Lamma Island in early 1975 (Melville). Although a common and pugnacious scavenger to inland areas in Europe this species is almost never seen away from the coast in Hong Kong.

[SAUNDERS' GULL *Larus saundersi* 黑嘴鷗
not illustrated
13". Winter visitor (November to April). Similar to Black-Headed Gull but has a black not chocolate brown head in summer. In all plumages has a short thick black bill and in flight has less black on the underside of the wings. Often seen in the Deep Bay area in small numbers, where adults are quite regular in March. Occasionally odd birds are met with elsewhere around the coast. DB]

HERRING GULL *Larus argentatus* 銀鷗
22". Winter visitor (October to April). Distinguished by large size and contrasting black wing tips in flight. First and second winter birds are heavily mottled brown. Two races occur, the darker yellow-legged (*mongolus*) and the pink-legged (*vegae*). Common in good numbers in coastal waters but usually favours less sheltered areas. A larger roost of both races can often be found at Nim Wan near Lau Fau Shan.

GREAT FRIGATE-BIRD *Fregata minor* 軍艦鳥
37". Summer visitor (May to September). Male entirely black with an inflatable red pouch at the base of the bill. Females are marked white below. Immatures are brown and white. Unmistakable silhouette. Graceful soaring flight, rarely flapping their wings. Oceanic. Breed on the Paracel Islands. Frigate-birds wander annually to Hong Kong, but in most cases specific identification is not possible either because of distance or the similarity of females and immatures of species that could occur here.

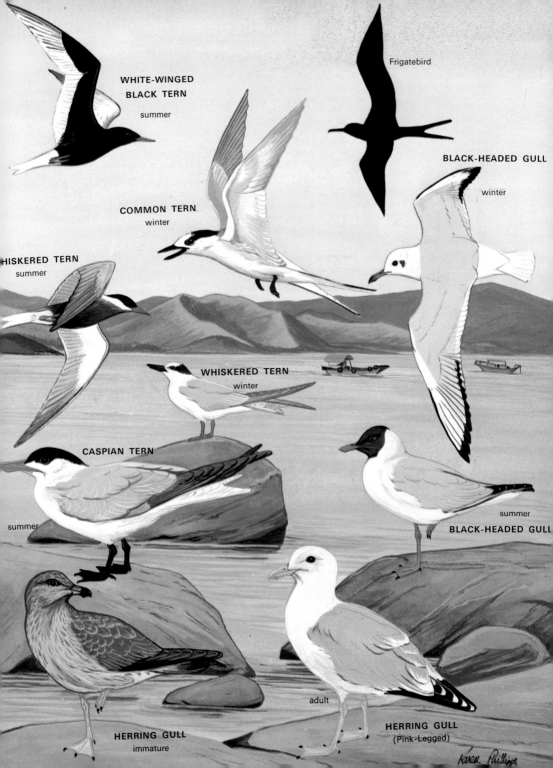

WHITE-WINGED BLACK TERN
summer

Frigatebird

BLACK-HEADED GULL
winter

COMMON TERN
winter

HISKERED TERN
summer

WHISKERED TERN
winter

CASPIAN TERN

summer

summer

BLACK-HEADED GULL

HERRING GULL
immature

adult

HERRING GULL
(Pink-Legged)

Karen Phillipps

UNCOMMON GULLS AND TERNS

BROWN-HEADED GULL *Larus brunnicephalus* 棕頭鷗
18". Winter visitor (November to February). Separated from other gulls by large white patch at base of primaries (headlights). Immatures and winter adults lack brown head. First identified in Victoria Harbour, November 1974 and since then has been seen regularly in small numbers. Probably previously overlooked.

BLACK-TAILED GULL *Larus crassirostris* 黑尾鷗
18". Winter visitor (November to April). Adult identified by dark mantle and broad black band on the tail. Immature has dark brown mantle, black tailband and pink bill tipped black. Also separated from immature Herring Gull by smaller size and washed brown head and breast, not streaked. Mostly immatures occur in Hong Kong. Generally scarce but regular in small numbers, particularly favours Tolo Harbour. The only gull which breeds on the China Coast.

BLACK-NAPED TERN *Sterna sumatrana* 黑枕海燕
12". (up to +2" for outer tail feathers). Passage migrant (April to June and September to November). Adult distinctive – a very pale tern. Flocks of up to 100 have been seen in spring and up to 800 in autumn after very bad weather. Reported from Deep Bay and Victoria Harbour. Absent in recent years and has not been seen since 1966, although once considered quite regular.

GULL-BILLED TERN *Gelochelidon nilotica* 鷗嘴海燕
15". Summer visitor (March to October). Short, stout black bill distinguishes this species from other terns. Appears whiter than most terns and only has a slightly forked tail. In winter the head is white with a small black patch near the eye. Regular; reported mainly from the Deep Bay area and Mirs Bay but is also seen occasionally in Victoria Harbour in rough weather. Occurs mostly in April, May and September, when flocks of up to 100 have been recorded.

LITTLE TERN *Sterna albifrons* 小海燕
9". Passage migrant (April to June and August to October). Separated from other terns by small size, narrow wings and more rapid wing beats. Often hovers. Mostly seen in the Deep Bay area but occasionally elsewhere. Regular in spring, when flocks of up to 40 have been seen, but scarce in autumn. DB

[GREATER CRESTED TERN *Sterna bergii* 大鳳頭海燕
not illustrated
18". Vagrant. Separated from other large terns by large greenish yellow bill, black crest, black feet and white forehead. Four widespread records of one or two birds. Should be looked for during and immediately after rough weather.]

[SOOTY TERN *Sterna fuscata* 烏燕鷗
not illustrated
17". Vagrant. Distinguished by black cap continuous with black mantle, white forehead and underparts. A large oceanic tern. Several were seen off Castle Peak during Typhoon Iris, September 1976.]

BROWN-HEADED GULL
adult

BLACK-TAILED GULL
adult

BLACK-NAPED TERN

GULL-BILLED TERN
summer

LITTLE TERN   summer

Ivan Phillips

KINGFISHERS AND HOOPOE

KINGFISHERS
Strikingly coloured. Large-headed with long pointed bills, short legs and tails. Rapid direct flight. Perch prominently in an upright posture. Usually solitary. Nest in burrows in banks. Eggs white and glossy.

PIED KINGFISHER   *Ceryle rudis*   斑點魚郎
12". Local resident.* Distinctive; could only be confused with larger and very rare Crested Kingfisher. Male has two black breast bands whereas the female has only one (often broken). Frequently hovers. Although once widespread is now virtually confined to the Deep Bay area and Starling Inlet; occasionally seen elsewhere around the coast during migration. Probably extinct as a local breeding species.

[**CRESTED KINGFISHER**   *Ceryle lugubris*   鳳頭魚郎
not illustrated
17". Occasional visitor. Similar to Pied Kingfisher but larger with fuller crest and completely barred tail. Secretive, keeping concealed in bushes overhanging fast streams. Formerly resident and probably bred in the Lam Tsuen Valley and in other areas with mountain streams. Last seen in 1968.   ]

COMMON KINGFISHER   *Alcedo atthis*   釣魚郎
7". Resident.* Distinctive; the familiar Kingfisher of Europe. Females and immatures are duller. Call is a high-pitched penetrating 'cheee.' Hovers. Not shy and often perches just above water-level. Common around the coast and along streams for most of the year, but is scarcer in midsummer. Breeds locally; a nesting burrow being made in a stream bank. The breeding season is March to July, usually two broods -- three to seven eggs.

BLACK-CAPPED KINGFISHER   *Halcyon pileata*   黑頭翡翠
12". Local resident.* Distinctive; note black cap and white collar. Mostly seen around the coast in winter when it returns annually to favoured localities. During the breeding season (spring and early summer) is found along streams in well-wooded areas but only a few pairs remain to breed in Hong Kong. Good places to look for this species are Hebe Haven and Lau Fau Shan in winter and the Tai Po Kau Forestry Reserve and upper Ho Chung Valley in summer.

WHITE-BREASTED KINGFISHER   *Halcyon smyrnensis*   白胸魚郎
11". Resident.* Distinctive chocolate brown underparts. Loud laughing call. Common and widespread during most of the year but local in summer. During the breeding season (April to June) is found inland where suitable sites for nesting burrows occur, often well away from watercourses. Single brooded – usually five eggs. Feeds principally on crabs, insects and lizards. The blue feathers were formerly used in South China for the manufacture of kingfisher enamel jewellery and skins were even exported for this purpose.

HOOPOE   *Upupa epops*   戴勝
12". Occasional visitor (March, May, August to November). Unmistakable. Name derived from call 'hoo poo poo.' Curious flapping flight like a butterfly. Single birds have been reported on at least ten occasions from widespread localities. Favours open grassland.

HOOPOE

PIED KINGFISHER

COMMON KINGFISHER

WHITE-BREASTED
KINGFISHER

BLACK-CAPPED
KINGFISHER

Karen Phillipps

BIRDS OF PREY

BLACK KITE (BLACK-EARED KITE) *Milvus migrans* 麻鷹
26″. Resident.* Slightly forked tail is diagnostic. Long angular wings. Distinctive 'flap, flap, glide' flight but often seen soaring high in company with several others. Tail twisted and turned in flight as a rudder. Shrill whistling call. A scavenger, particularly favouring Victoria Harbour but can be found almost anywhere. Much commoner in winter when the population is about 1000 compared with 200 in summer (Melville). Large winter roosts, principally at Stonecutters' Island, Victoria Peak and Ma Nam Wat, where several hundred can be seen circling at dusk. Most summering birds are non-breeding visitors but an estimated 15 pairs breed. Large stick nests lined with paper are built, usually in trees. The breeding season is January to April, single brooded – two or three eggs. Considered to be the major birdstrike hazard species at Kai Tak Airport (Melville). Probably the most numerous bird of prey of its size in the world. 🐦 ⋙ △ ▲ ≋ ᒐ ✦

BUZZARD *Buteo buteo* 鵟
20–22″. Winter visitor (September to April). Usually pale below with black patches on the forewing but variable. Wings broad and rounded. Tail also rounded and often fanned. Soars in wide circles. Will hover occasionally. Often seen perched on overhead wires. Widespread and fairly common. Known to take poultry. 🐦 ⋙ △ ▲ ✦

KESTREL *Falco tinnunculus* 紅隼
13½″. Winter visitor (September to April). Distinctive rufous upperparts. Long wings and tail. Typical small falcon. Hovers frequently. Widespread but favours open country. Fairly common most years. 🐦 ⋙ △ ▲ ✦

PEREGRINE FALCON *Falco peregrinus* 遊隼
15–19″. Local resident.* Large falcon with pronounced black moustachial streak. Distinctive anchor outline in flight. Pigeon-like flight but stoops steeply in a power dive on prey. Widespread, even being seen in urban areas where it roosts on tall buildings during the day. At least one pair breeds in the Tolo Harbour area and it is likely that two or three other eyries exist in remote areas. The nest is constructed of sticks on a cliff and used year after year. The breeding season is March and April. Birds as large as duck are killed as prey. In other parts of the world this species has declined drastically, apparently due to the effects of poisonous chemicals on its prey but is also much prized by falconers. 🐦 △ ▲ ᒐ ✦

COLLARED SCOPS OWL *Otus bakkamoena* 領角貓頭鷹
9″. Local resident.* Virtually the only owl in Hong Kong. The call is a soft mellow 'hoo-o', repeated four or five times per minute, mainly heard in January and February. Nocturnal. Widespread, but has declined in recent years. Apparently still quite common on Hong Kong Island, although rarely seen. Nests in old Magpie nests. The breeding season is March to May – two to five eggs. 🐦 🌲 ⋙

[BARRED OWLET *Glaucidium cuculoides* 鴝鵅
not illustrated
9″. Former resident.* Barring of head and underparts and yellow eyes distinguishes this species from Collared Scops Owl. Laughing whooping call like a Red Indian war cry. Largely diurnal. Odd birds are still occasionally seen or heard in the Lam Tsuen Valley and it is just possible that a single pair may still be resident. 🌲 ⋙]

[BROWN FISH-OWL *Ketupa zeylonensis* 褐魚貓頭鷹
not illustrated
21″. Occasional visitor. Distinguished from Eagle Owl by lack of facial disc. Nocturnal. Spends much time on the ground, usually near watercourses. Formerly resident in the Pok Fu Lam area. Last recorded in 1970. 🌲 ≋]

[EAGLE-OWL *Bubo bubo* 巨貓頭鷹
not illustrated
22″. Occasional visitor. Enormous, almost eagle-sized bird. Prominent ear tufts and facial disc. Active at dawn and dusk. Capable of killing a small deer. Last recorded 1978 🌲 △]

BLACK VULTURE *Aegypius monachus* 禿鷲
41″. Occasional winter visitor (December to March). Huge. Adults entirely very dark brown (appear black). Distinctive flight silhouette and has appropriately been called the 'flying barn door' (Webster). Soars masterfully. Tail is wedge-shaped but is often worn through being dragged on the ground. One or two have been quite regularly recorded at Long Valley or Deep Bay in recent winters. Previously, their appearance usually coincided with an abundance of carrion in the area. ✦

Black Vulture

Buzzard

Black Kite

COLLARED
COPS OWL

immature
Peregrine Falcon

Kestrel

adult

KESTREL

KESTREL
♂

PEREGRINE FALCON

BUZZARD

BLACK KITE

Karen Phillips

EAGLES, HARRIERS AND OSPREY

IMPERIAL EAGLE *Aquila heliaca* 白肩鵰
31–33". Winter visitor (October to April). Adult is blackish brown with buffish crown and nape. Usually white patches on scapulars and grey base to tail. Regular in small numbers to the northern New Territories; most often seen at Long Valley.

GOLDEN EAGLE *Aquila chrysaëtos* 金鵰
33". Occasional winter visitor (December to March) Adult is dark brown with tawny crown and nape. Immatures have distinctive white and black tail pattern. Tail is longer and larger than other 'dark eagles.' Formerly, quite regularly recorded in small numbers in the northern New Territories but has become scarce in recent years.

[STEPPE EAGLE *Aquila rapax* 草原鵰
not illustrated
30–34". Occasional winter visitor (October to April). Adults almost uniformly dark brown but yellowish patch on nape separates this species from Spotted Eagle. Immatures have two distinctive white bands along the centre and trailing edge of the wing. Quite regularly recorded in small numbers in the northern New Territories; most often seen at Long Valley.

[SPOTTED EAGLE *Aquila clanga* 烏鵰
not illustrated
26–29". Occasional winter visitor (October to April). Adults are very dark, most having a small white patch on the upper tail-coverts. First and second year birds have conspicuous white spots on upperparts (hence name). Compact; smaller than Imperial, Golden and Steppe Eagles, with a very short tail. Often seen on the ground. Scarce visitor to the northern New Territories.

WHITE-BELLIED SEA-EAGLE *Haliaeetus leucogaster* 白腹海鵰
28". Local resident.* Adult distinctive. Immature is brownish but usually has a white base to the tail. When soaring, wings are held in a shallow 'V.' Virtually confined to coastal areas and rarely seen inland. A few pairs breed or attempt to do so annually. The eyrie is a huge structure, constructed of sticks on a cliff ledge, used and added to year after year. The breeding season is from December to February. This species is best looked for along the remoter shores of the New Territories; particularly favours the Sai Kung Peninsula and small rocky offshore islands.

BONELLI'S EAGLE *Hieraaëtus fasciatus* 白腹山鵰
25–27". Local resident.* Adult has distinctive dark brown and white pattern on underside; also whitish patch on nape, scapulars and back which is variable in extent. Immatures are browner with pale chestnut underparts. Flight silhouette shows long tail and small but protruding head. Fond of aerobatics. Aggresive. Often seen in pairs. A few pairs breed in the remoter hilly areas of the New Territories and occasionally on the larger offshore islands. Usually nest on rocky outcrops, utilizing the same eyrie year after year. The breeding season is from February to April.

OSPREY *Pandion haliaetus* 魚鷹
20–23". Non-breeding visitor. Distinctive white head and neck with broad black band through eye to nape. Marked kink to wings. Hovers over water and plunges feet first for prey. Often seen carrying fish. Fond of perching on stakes in shallows. Primarily a regular winter visitor to the Deep Bay area, in small numbers, but can occasionally be seen elsewhere around the coast. Odd birds occur in summer at Plover Cove Reservoir.

EASTERN MARSH HARRIER *Circus aeruginosus spilonotus* 澤鵟
19–22". Winter visitor (September to April). Full adult males are uncommon but have distinctive pale head, brown and grey wings and variable amounts of streaking. Young males are much more usual and are browner with pale head and scapulars and white rump. Females are generally brown above. Hunts low over the ground with wings held in a shallow 'V.' Common in the Deep Bay area but rare elsewhere. DB

[PIED HARRIER *Circus melanoleucos* 鵲鵟
not illustrated
17–18". Occasional winter visitor (September to April). Adult male is distinctively pied black, white and grey. Females and immatures are smaller than Eastern Marsh Harrier but are difficult to separate. Scarce visitor to the Deep Bay area, but possibly regular on passage in very small numbers. DB]

Bonelli's Eagle   adult

Imperial Eagle
adult

White-Bellied Sea-Eagle
adult

mature
en Eagle

Eastern Marsh Harrier

OSPREY

WHITE-BELLIED SEA-EAGLE
adult

BONELLI'S EAGLE   adult

EASTERN MARSH HARRIER
♂

Karen Phillipps

BIRDS OF PREY

SPARROWHAWK *Accipiter nisus* 鷂
13–15". Winter visitor (September to May). Males have upperparts dark brownish-grey and below are white narrowly barred with rufous. Short rounded wings and long tail are distinctive. Often makes typical quick dash at bush level. Found in both open and wooded country and is even known to have attacked cagebirds on balconies. Scarce but regular in small numbers, mainly on passage. Widespread. Females were formerly used for falconry in China, principally to catch Quail. 🏠 🌲 ⋙ 🐟

[JAPANESE SPARROWHAWK *Accipiter gularis* 松雀鷹
not illustrated
10–12". Vagrant. Not safely separated in the field from Sparrowhawk or Besra (*A. virgatus*) (which could occur) although smaller. One captured and several uncertain sight records from widespread areas. Probably regular. Resident in Kwangtung Province.]

[GOSHAWK *Accipiter gentilis* 蒼鷹
not illustrated
19–24". Winter visitor (October to April). Similar to Sparrowhawk but separated by large size and prominent broad whitish eyebrow in all plumages. Found in both open and wooded country but prefers the latter. One or two are seen most years, principally at the Tai Po Kau Forestry Reserve. 🌲 🐟 ♣]

SERPENT EAGLE *Spilornis cheela* 蛇鵰
28". Non-breeding visitor. In flight adult shows dark brown colouration with broad white wing band and broad white tail band. Immatures have white underparts often with blackish markings which sometimes form a band across the upper breast. Often perch high in dead trees. Soar to great heights. Screaming call. Seen annually in ones or twos in the New Territories, particularly favouring the Lam Tsuen Valley and Sai Kung Peninsula. Resident in Kwangtung Province. A known poultry thief. 🌲 ⋙ 🐟 ♣

BLACK BAZA *Aviceda leuphotes* 鳳頭鵑鷹
13". Vagrant (May, June). Unmistakable. Wings broad and rounded. Flapping crow-like flight, usually for short distances just above tree canopy. More active at dawn and dusk. Screaming call. Favours forest clearings. Several records of up to three birds in the adjacent Tai Po Kau Forestry Reserve and Shing Mun Plantation. 🌲

HOBBY *Falco subbuteo* 燕隼
12–14". Non-breeding visitor. Adult like small Peregrine Falcon but with chestnut on thighs and beneath tail. Immatures are browner. Appears swift-like in flight with long scythe-shaped wings and short tail. Scarce in recent years but one or two recorded annually, usually on passage. Can occur almost anywhere. Follows migrating flocks of swallows upon which it preys. Resident in Kwangtung Province. 🌲 🐟 ♣ ⤫

[MERLIN *Falco columbarius* 灰背隼
not illustrated
11–13". Winter visitor (October to March). Similar to Hobby but smaller and lacks moustachial streak. Male has dark grey upperparts with broad black sub-terminal band on tail; underparts are buff with narrow streaks. Females are like small Kestrels but darker brown. Flies low over ground and bushes. Widespread but keeps to open country. Very scarce but odd birds occur in most years. 🐟 ♣ ⤫]

GREY-FACED BUZZARD-EAGLE *Butastur indicus* 屎鷹
17". Occasional winter visitor (November to April). In flight like a large broad-winged falcon; shows black stripe on white throat, brown breast and tail closely barred in the centre only. About twelve records from widespread areas, but favours the Tai Po Kau Forestry Reserve. 🌲 🐟 ♣

Sparrowhawk
♂

SERPENT EAGLE   adult

SPARROWHAWK
immature

HOBBY   adult

BLACK BAZA

GREY-FACED
BUZZARD-EAGLE

PARAKEET, COCKATOO, BARBET, ROLLER AND WRYNECK

ROSE-RINGED PARAKEET *Psittacula krameri* 紅領綠鸚鵡
16½". Local resident.* Distinctive, but other exotic parakeets (which have certainly escaped from captivity) are occasionally recorded in an apparently wild state. Females lack the rose pink collar. Call is a harsh rather shrill screech. Flight is swift and straight. Forms communal roosts in the evenings (notably in the Banyan trees (*Ficus retusa*) in Sports Road, Happy Valley). In spring, enjoys tearing the flowers of Cotton Trees (*Bombax malabaricum*). Apparently introduced about 1900, although could have established itself naturally through expansion of range (La Touche). Flocks are regularly seen in urban Hong Kong and Kowloon but is much more local in the New Territories where it particularly favours the Mong Tseng Peninsula. Nests in holes in trees but breeding has not been proved for some years. ● 🌲 🏠

[**BUDGERIGAR** *Melopsittacus undulatus*
not illustrated
7–8". Escape. A familiar cagebird which is naturally green but other varieties are common. Single birds or even pairs are quite regularly seen flying free, often associating with other species.]

SULPHUR-CRESTED COCKATOO *Cacatua sulphurea*
19–20". Introduced.* Unmistakable. Two sub-species occur, distinguishable by the intensity of yellow/orange of the crest. Call is a harsh raucous screech. About 30, usually in one or two flocks, range from Happy Valley to Pok Fu Lam on the north side of Hong Kong Island. A flock of about ten can invariably be found in Victoria Barracks, where in spring, like the Rose-ringed Parakeets, they enjoy tearing the flowers of Cotton Trees (*Bombax malabaricum*). Occasionally recorded elsewhere, particularly on Stonecutters' Island. There are two recent isolated breeding records, but in view of the longevity of this species it is not known whether the population is self-sustaining. Detailed records have been kept since 1961 but the first introduction of this species is not known for certain. However, one theory is that the original birds were released from Flagstaff House (where they were kept as pets) in 1941 just prior to the Japanese Occupation. ● 🌲

GREAT BARBET *Megalaima virens* 大擬啄木
13". Local resident.* Unmistakable although difficult to see as it keeps to tree-tops, never visiting the ground. Heavy rising and falling flight. Two monotonous and continually repeated calls – 'coo-ee-you' by the male and the answering 'ee-ee-ee' by the female. These calls can be kept up for several minutes, which by sheer length separates them from similar calls of the Koel. When several call together the sound has been accurately described as 'demonical howling' (Herklots). Found throughout the New Territories, wherever substantial woodland exists, particularly favouring the larger 'fung shui' woods and older plantations. Lam Tsuen Valley and the Tai Po Kau Forestry Reserve are good areas to find this species. Although once regular it is now apparently absent on Hong Kong Island. Nests in holes in trees. The breeding season is March to August, two or three broods – three to five white eggs. 🌲

BROAD-BILLED ROLLER (DOLLARBIRD) *Eurystomus orientalis* 三寶鳥
12". Passage migrant (April to May, September to November). Distinctive but colours vary depending on the light. In flight shows conspicuous silvery blue circular patches (dollars) on wings. Often appears as a black bird carrying a red chili (Boonsong Lekagul). Immature has a black bill. Perches conspicuously, flying up to catch insects on the wing. Mostly seen singly but occasionally occurs in small parties. Widespread and regular but not common. Favours open country and woods. More often seen in autumn. 🌲 🏠 ⛰

WRYNECK *Jynx torquilla* 蚊鴷
7½". Winter visitor (September to April). Appears all grey-brown with a darker eye-stripe. Twists neck at odd angles (hence name). Commonly feeds on the ground but also perches on branches when it is difficult to see. Nearly always seen singly. Widespread, favouring areas with thick scrub and low bushes. ● 🏠

ROSE-RINGED PARAKEET

GREAT BARBET

SULPHUR-CRESTED
COCKATOO

BROAD-BILLED ROLLER
adult

WRYNECK

Karen Phillips

DOVES

Familiar plump birds with small heads and bills. Tail slightly rounded. Short legs. Strong direct flight. Soft cooing calls. Usually feed on the ground. Regarded as game birds in Hong Kong and are still shot in large numbers. Neck markings are an important aid to identification.

SPOTTED DOVE *Streptopelia chinensis* 珠頸斑鳩
12″. Resident.* White-spotted black collar around hind-neck is diagnostic. Conspicuous white-tipped outer tail feathers, noticeable in flight. Often seen on roads and paths. Wing clapping sometimes heard when flushed. Usually only a few together but flocks are occasionally seen in hard weather. Very common and widespread being found virtually everywhere. Tamer on Hong Kong Island where it cannot be shot. Regarded as a pest in the New Territories as it consumes large quantities of rice at harvest time. Breeds throughout the year, usually constructing a flimsy nest in a bush or tree a few feet off the ground. A clutch comprises two eggs. The male performs a vertical display flight rising some 200 feet and coming down with wings and tail stiffly extended.

RUFOUS TURTLE-DOVE *Streptopelia orientalis* 山斑鳩
12½″. Winter visitor (August to May). Black patches with whitish bars (not continuous) on each side of neck are diagnostic. Narrow grey tips on the underside of all tail feathers form a complete band. Regular and widespread; favours areas with scattered trees and good secondary growth. Much scarcer and local in recent years.

RED TURTLE-DOVE *Streptopelia tranquebarica* 火斑鳩
9″. Passage migrant (April, September to November). Red upperparts with contrasting grey head distinguishes the male. Females are duller with only a red tinge. Small size, short tail and plump body distinctive. Thin black ring on hind neck is diagnostic but often difficult to see. Usually in flocks. Scarce but regular and widespread in autumn; favours lowland cultivated areas.

EMERALD DOVE *Chalcophaps indica* 翠翅鳩
10″. Local resident. Distinctive. Female similar but with brown nape and crown. Usually on the ground. Shy, quiet and alert. Favours thick woodland with good secondary growth. One or two apparently resident in the Tai Po Kau Forestry Reserve but breeding has not been proved. Occasionally single birds are seen elsewhere. Although it is considered that genuinely wild birds have been recorded, this species is also known to have been deliberately released.

FERAL PIGEON *Columba livia* 原鴿
13″. Introduced. Plumage variable but usual form is blue-grey with two broad black wing bars. All are descendants of domestic stock. Compared with other cities the urban areas hold very few feral pigeons although domestic pigeons are commonly seen flying in small tight flocks.

SPOTTED DOVE

RUFOUS TURTLE-DOVE

RED TURTLE-DOVE

FERAL PIGEON

EMERALD DOVE

Kozx Phillipps

CUCKOOS

Slender, hawk-like birds with long graduated tails and slightly decurved bills. Shy and difficult to observe as they keep to the tree-tops. All have distinctive calls which are heard in spring and early summer. Swift flight. Parasitic, except coucals.

PLAINTIVE CUCKOO *Cacomantis merulinus* 八聲杜鵑
8½". Summer visitor,* (odd birds recorded at any time). Small size distinctive. Also a hepatic red-brown barred blackish form. A plaintive eight note call—four slow notes followed by four descending rapid double notes. Also a 'pee po pee-ee' call. The calls are repeated constantly, even at night, and can be most annoying. Quite common and widespread in spring and summer but otherwise rather scarce. Parasitises Long-Tailed Tailor-Birds, but it remains a mystery as to how the cuckoo gets her eggs inside the nests. One theory is that they are laid first on the ground, then placed inside the nest by the cuckoo using her bill.

KOEL *Eudynamis scolopacea* 噪鵑
17". Resident.* Pale bill and deep red eyes are distinctive. More often heard than seen. Call is 'ko-el' repeated five to ten times. The second note is longer and louder, each repeated call gets slightly higher until the bird has to stop. Also a loud ringing laughing call comprising up to eight repeated notes. Quite common and widespread being noticed particularly in spring and early summer. Favours open areas with scattered trees, even urban parks. Parasitises Black-Necked Starlings and where these do not occur probably Crested Mynahs.

INDIAN CUCKOO *Cuculus micropterus* 四聲杜鵑
13". Summer visitor* (April to October). Distinguished from similar-sized cuckoos by brown mantle and contrasting grey head. Call is 'ko-ko-ta-ko' (fourth note lower) repeated and becoming higher in pitch. Also interpreted as 'one more bottle' (Herklots). Locally common in lightly wooded areas of the New Territories, especially favouring Fanling Golf Course. Parasitises Black Drongos.

[**CUCKOO** *Cuculus canorus* 杜鵑
not illustrated
13". Passage migrant (April, May, September and October). Upperparts greyer than Indian Cuckoo and underparts white banded with narrow dark grey bars. Call 'cuc-coo.' Very scarce in recent years but probably overlooked. This is the familiar Cuckoo of Europe.

[**HIMALAYAN CUCKOO** *Cuculus saturatus* 中杜鵑
not illustrated
13". Passage migrant (April, May and October). Very similar to Cuckoo. Underparts buff with usually broader and more widely spaced bars than Cuckoo. Call is four dull booming notes 'hoo-hoo-hoo-hoo.' Very shy usually keeping to tree-tops. Only seen in ones and twos. A very scarce spring visitor but has been recorded from widespread areas.

[**LARGE HAWK-CUCKOO** *Cuculus sparverioides* 鷹頭杜鵑
not illustrated
16". Summer visitor (March to June). Distinguished by large size and rufous breast streaked buff and dark brown. Call 'pi-pee-ha' repeated over and over again, gradually becoming frantic. Usually heard in April. Recorded annually at the Tai Po Kau Forestry Reserve and Shing Mun Plantation where it probably breeds.

GREATER COUCAL (CROW-PHEASANT) *Centropus sinensis* 毛雞
21". Resident.* Striking chestnut wings on otherwise black plumage. Immatures are similar but with varying amounts of barring. Call is the familiar 'poomp' 'poomp' 'poomp' repeated and a chuckle which sounds like water emptying from a bottle. Calls from bush-tops but spends much of its time on the ground or clambering around in thickets. Common and widespread. In May or June constructs a large untidy domed nest, usually on the ground in undergrowth. Eats almost anything. Highly valued in Chinese medicine.

LESSER COUCAL (LESSER CROW-PHEASANT) *Centropus bengalensis* 小毛雞
15". Resident.* Smaller and less striking version of Greater Coucal. Immatures resemble non-breeding birds. Call is a monotonous 'currah' 'currah' 'currah.' Widespread but less common than Greater Coucal. Favours scrub and tree-covered hillsides.

PLAINTIVE CUCKOO

KOEL
♀

INDIAN CUCKOO

KOEL
♂

GREATER COUCAL
adult

adult
LESSER COUCAL

LESSER COUCAL
non-breeding

Karen Phillipps

RARE NON-PASSERINES

RED-WINGED CRESTED CUCKOO *Clamator coromandus* 紅翅鳳頭杜鵑
18″. Occasional visitor (April, September and October). Distinctive, but if only glimpsed could be confused with a coucal. Calls are a series of raucous screams. Found in woodland or dense scrubland where it is difficult to see. Five records from widespread areas.

BLUE-TAILED BEE-EATER *Merops philippinus* 栗喉蜂虎
12″. Vagrant (April, May). Unmistakable. Feeds on flying insects caught on brief sallies from an exposed perch. Four records of up to seven birds from widespread areas

BLACK-NAPED GREEN WOODPECKER *Picus canus* 綠啄木鳥
13″. Occasional visitor. Unmistakable. Female lacks crimson forehead. Drums frequently on trees, particularly in spring. Loud laughing call. About twenty records, mostly from the Lam Tsuen Valley. Has become scarcer in recent years.

RUFOUS WOODPECKER *Micropternus brachyurus* 栗啄木鳥
10″. Occasional visitor (November to April). Unmistakable. Female lacks red cheek patch. Drums on trees. Loud laughing call. Lives extensively on ants and is said to smell strongly of formic acid. One or two birds have been recorded on at least twelve occasions in the Lam Tsuen Valley and once at Repulse Bay.

CHINESE PITTA *Pitta nympha* 藍翅八色鶫
8″. Vagrant (April and July). Unmistakable. Secretive and difficult to observe as it keeps to the ground in thick undergrowth. Runs away when alarmed. Noisy whirring flight; shows conspicuous white wing patches. Call is a clear double whistle. Two records, both of single birds on Hong Kong Island.

BLUE-TAILED BEE-EATER

RED-WINGED
CRESTED CUCKOO

RUFOUS WOODPECKER

BLACK-NAPED
GREEN WOODPECKER

CHINESE PITTA

Karen-Phillipps

SWIFTS, SWALLOWS, MARTINS AND NIGHTJARS

SWIFTS
Long scythe-like wings. Rapid flight. Gregarious. Almost exclusively aerial except when breeding. Never perch on trees or overhead wires. Twittering calls.

LARGE WHITE-RUMPED SWIFT *Apus pacificus* 白腰雨燕
7½". Resident. Separated from House Swift by larger size, deeply forked tail and more leisurely flight. Numbers fluctuate but is usually commoner in summer. Widespread, but favours hill-tops and offshore islands where it probably breeds.

HOUSE SWIFT *Apus affinis* 小白腰雨燕
6". Resident.* Identified by small size and very shallow fork to tail which often looks square. Common and widespread. Breeds in colonies throughout the urban areas and market towns of the New Territories. Nests are constructed under eaves, beams and ledges in May and June, single brooded—two eggs.

[WHITE-THROATED NEEDLETAIL *Hirundapus caudacutus* 針尾雨燕
not illustrated
8". Vagrant. Large swift with white throat and conspicuous white horseshoe on underparts. Plumage generally black but with greyish mantle. First recorded April, 1977 over Fanling. Should occur annually on passage and has probably been overlooked.

SWALLOWS AND MARTINS
Wings straight, shorter and broader than swifts. Regularly perch on overhead wires. Graceful flight. Often feed low over the ground.

SWALLOW *Hirundo rustica* 家燕
6". Summer visitor* but recorded locally throughout the year. Immatures lack elongated outer tail feathers. Very common and widespread in summer. Scarce from October to February when it is usually only seen over fish-ponds in the Deep Bay area. Nests are constructed of mud under eaves of houses or on specially erected shelves. Villagers consider Swallows lucky and encourage them to nest. Breeding commences on arrival and is usually completed by June.

RED-RUMPED SWALLOW *Hirundo daurica* 金腰燕
7". Winter visitor (August to May). Separated from Swallow by pale, often reddish, rump. Colour of underparts is variable depending on the race. Usually seen on passage when it is gregarious. Regular visitor to open areas in the New Territories but is never particularly common.

HOUSE MARTIN *Delichon urbica* 毛脚燕
5¼". Irregular passage migrant (February to May, September to November). Prominent white rump. Usually only odd birds are recorded but occasionally large flocks are seen. Very scarce, but recorded from widespread areas.

SAND MARTIN *Riparia riparia* 沙燕
5". Passage migrant (September to January, April to June). Brown upperparts and breast band are diagnostic. Only recorded in small numbers. Scarce but regular visitor to the Deep Bay area. DB

NIGHTJARS
Exclusively nocturnal birds which hawk insects. Long pointed wings and very agile flight. During the day only seen when flushed from the ground or sitting horizontally along a branch. Extremely well camouflaged at rest. Although once locally common in parts of the New Territories nightjars are now very scarce and their status unknown. It is thought that a few pairs still breed in the less developed parts of the northern New Territories. Specific identification is difficult.

JAPANESE NIGHTJAR *Caprimulgus indicus* 夜鷹
11". Local resident.* Separated from Savannah Nightjar by darker colouration and only white spots on tips of tail feathers. Call is a rapid repeated 'chuck-chuck-chuck-chuck.' Breeding was proved on Ma On Shan in 1938.

[SAVANNAH NIGHTJAR *Caprimulgus affinis* 林夜鷹
not illustrated
10". Local resident. Male has prominent white outer tail feathers. Female is paler but with no white in tail. Call is like a whiplash cutting the air.

LARGE WHITE-RUMPED SWIFT

HOUSE SWIFT

SWALLOW
adult

ND MARTIN

HOUSE MARTIN

RED-RUMPED
SWALLOW

JAPANESE NIGHTJAR

Karen Phillips

SHRIKES, DRONGOS AND ORIOLE

SHRIKES

Medium-sized birds with strong, hooked bills. In adult plumage all have thick black eye-stripe. Longish tail; waved around when at rest. Sexes are alike. Perch prominently. Prey on insects, small animals and young birds, which are usually pounced upon. Mostly solitary and aggressive towards other shrikes. Calls are harsh, scolding and discordant.

BROWN SHRIKE *Lanius cristatus* 紅尾伯勞

7¾". Non-breeding visitor. Variable as at least three races occur; a small brownish shrike with paler underparts will almost certainly be this species. Some have a thin white eyebrow above the black eye-stripe which is diagnostic. Immatures often have the underparts barred. Regular in small numbers but has become much scarcer in recent years. Not usually seen in June and July. Widespread, favours open country but can even be found in built-up areas in winter.

[BULL-HEADED SHRIKE *Lanius bucephalus* 牛頭伯勞
not illustrated

8". Occasional visitor (September to April). Similar to Brown Shrike but has a white patch at the base of the primaries, which is conspicuous in flight. Odd birds have been recorded from widespread localities, but there have been no definite sightings for several years.]

CHINESE GREAT GREY SHRIKE *Lanius sphenocercus* 楔尾伯勞

11". Vagrant. Distinctive. Hovers frequently and will take prey in the air. Three records.

RUFOUS-BACKED SHRIKE *Lanius schach* 棕背伯勞

10". Resident.* Distinctive handsome appearance. Frequently perches on overhead wires. Noisy scolding call but can mimic other species quite pleasantly. Common and widespread; favours open country. Unless large gardens and playing fields are available tends to avoid urban areas. A melanistic variety known as the DUSKY SHRIKE is fairly common. These shrikes are iron grey and black but as they interbreed freely with normals, intermediate varieties are seen. The breeding season is March to June, four to six eggs are laid in a cup shaped nest constructed in a bush or tree.

DRONGOS

Medium sized birds with distinctive tails. Wings long and pointed. Bill and legs black. Perch in exposed places, flying up to catch insects on the wing. Noisy and pugnacious.

HAIR-CRESTED DRONGO *Dicrurus hottentottus* 髮冠捲尾

13". Summer visitor,* but occasionally recorded in winter. Strongly upturned outer tail feathers (best seen in flight) with virtually no fork to tail and overall prominent sheen separates this species from Black Drongo. The hair crest is difficult to see in the field. Fairly common between April and October but confined to well wooded areas; particularly favours the Lam Tsuen Valley and the Tai Po Kau Forestry Reserve. Breeding commences in May, when a cup shaped nest is constructed high up in a tree or bamboo thicket. Three eggs are usually laid—single brooded.

BLACK DRONGO *Dicrurus macrocercus* 黑捲尾

11". Summer visitor,* but also recorded in winter in much smaller numbers. Deeply forked tail separates this species from Hair-Crested Drongo. Immatures can have whitish markings on the underparts. Unusual cat-like hissing call. Perches prominently, often on overhead wires and backs of cattle. Fairly common and widespread between March and October. Favours open country with scattered trees and is particularly numerous on the larger offshore islands, notably Stonecutters' Island and Cheung Chau. Breeds in May and June when three or four eggs are laid in a cup shaped nest constructed in the fork of a tree. Mobs crows and in India is known as King Crow.

BLACK-NAPED ORIOLE *Oriolus chinensis* 黑枕黃鸝

10½". Summer visitor,* but odd birds are seen in winter. Unmistakable but females are duller. 'Appear as golden butterflies' (Herklots). Call is a cheerful fluty 'we-weeleow.' Returns to favoured localities between April and September every year. Prefers open country with scattered trees and is thinly distributed throughout the New Territories; scarce in recent years on Hong Kong Island. Fanling Golf Course, where several pairs breed annually, is the best area to locate this species. Often nests in association with Black Drongos (for protection). The nest is a deep cup slung within the fork of a branch near its extremity, high in a tree (often pine). Breeds from April to June, single brooded—two to four eggs.

BROWN SHRIKE

HAIR-CRESTED DRONGO

Chinese Great Grey Shrike

BLACK DRONGO

RUFOUS-BACKED
SHRIKE

BLACK-NAPED ORIOLE

BLACK-NAPED
ORIOLE

immature

Karen Phillips

GREY DRONGOS AND STARLINGS

GREY DRONGO *Dicrurus leucophaeus* 灰捲尾
$11\frac{1}{2}''$. Winter visitor (September to April). As Black Drongo, but is plain grey of varying shades. Two races occur, the uniform grey Ashy Drongo (r. *salangensis*) and the White-Cheeked Drongo (r. *leucogenis*). Scarce but regular in very small numbers; favours open country with scattered trees such as the Lam Tsuen Valley.

STARLINGS AND MYNAHS

Medium-sized, stocky land birds with short tails and strong pointed bills. Steady and direct flight. Gregarious. Intelligent.

GREY STARLING *Sturnus cineraceus* 灰椋鳥
$9\frac{1}{2}''$. Winter visitor (October to April). Generally much browner than Silky and Chinese Starlings. Distinguished from Silky Starling by dark crown, white forehead and cheeks and white band across rump. Normally in small flocks. Uncommon but widespread in the New Territories, particularly favours the Deep Bay area. Prefers open country, usually near the coast.

CHINESE STARLING *Sturnus sinensis* 噪林鳥
$8''$. Local resident.* Large white patches on wings of males are diagnostic. Females are similar but the shoulder patch is less distinct. Immatures closely resemble Silky Starling but are smaller and generally in flocks with adults. Rarely on the ground. Flocks of varying sizes are seen throughout the year in widespread areas, but nowhere is this species common. Small flocks nest in crevices in buildings or occasionally in holes in trees. Breeding takes place in May, single brooded—four or five eggs.

SILKY STARLING *Sturnus sericeus* 絲光椋鳥
$9\frac{1}{2}''$. Winter visitor (September to April). Distinguished from Grey Starling by uniform grey head. Females are duller. Often in large flocks, sometimes several hundred strong. Quite common and widespread being found in open areas but particularly favouring coastal mangroves.

BLACK-NECKED STARLING *Sturnus nigricollis* 黑領椋鳥
$11''$. Local resident.* Distinctive pied appearance. Black collar absent on immatures. Nick-named the 'hurdy-gurdy bird' because of its loud cheerful piping cry 'chee-we-chee chee-we-chee.' Occurs only in the northern and eastern parts of the New Territories where it is common, but appears to be expanding its range. Until recently, absent on Hong Kong Island but now regularly reported at Stanley. Particularly common at Fanling Golf Course where there is a large evening roost in summer. A conspicuous large nest is constructed high in a tree. The breeding season is April to August, up to three broods—three to five eggs.

GREY STARLING

GREY DRONGO
(Ashy)

GREY DRONGO
(White-Cheeked)

CHINESE STARLING

SILKY STARLING

adult

BLACK-NECKED STARLING

MYNAHS, STARLING AND JAY

CRESTED MYNAH *Acridotheres cristatellus* 八哥

10½". Resident.* Distinctive white wing patches seen in flight. Very common and widespread. Often found near and perched on cattle but occurs almost everywhere. Forms noisy evening roosts usually in Banyan trees (*Ficus retusa*). A hole nesting species; particularly favours weepholes in retaining walls and cutting slopes. The breeding season is from April to July, two broods—four to seven eggs. A popular cagebird which can be taught to talk.   🏠 ⅩⅩⅩ 🦅 ♣♣

EUROPEAN STARLING *Sturnus vulgaris* 紫翅椋鳥

8½". Local winter visitor (October to February). The familiar Starling of Europe, North America and Australasia. Since 1971/72 a small flock of up to eleven has wintered in an area of rough grazing at Lok Ma Chau. This species appears to have arrived by normal expansion of range and not by introduction. Its arrival was not welcomed as in places where it has been introduced, such as North America, it has proved to be a considerable pest. However, initial fears have not been realised as in six winters numbers have remained static and it has not been seen outside the small area of its discovery.   ♣♣ DB

COMMON MYNAH *Acridotheres tristis* 家八哥

10". Local resident.* Adults are distinctive with dark brown body, black head, yellow bill, feet and orbital skin. Immatures are duller. Apparently introduced. First recorded January, 1952 and seen regularly since. In 1959 as many as 30 were together in one flock but since then numbers have declined steadily. The few remaining birds are usually reported from Mong Tseng, San Tin or Shek Kong. It is surprising that this species is apparently dying out as when it has been introduced elsewhere, such as in the Seychelles, it has rapidly established itself often at the expense of the indigenous avifauna.   ⅩⅩⅩ 🦅 ♣♣

INDIAN GRACKLE *Gracula religiosa* 鷯哥

12". Introduced. Distinctive. Immatures do not have yellow lappets. The most common call is a loud piercing whistle. Often perch conspicuously in tall trees. A popular cagebird which is regularly seen flying wild, singly or in pairs. There is no evidence of breeding but a feral self-supporting population may become established. The best talker amongst the mynahs.   🏠 🌲 ⅩⅩⅩ 🦅

JAY *Garrulus glandarius* 松鴉

13". Non-breeding visitor. Distinctive. Harsh scolding screeching call. One or two winter annually and occasionally odd birds remain throughout the summer but breeding has not been proved. Recorded mostly in established woodlands, particularly in the Lam Tsuen Valley, Tai Po Kau Forestry Reserve and Shing Mun Plantation.   🌲 ⅩⅩⅩ

CRESTED MYNAH

EUROPEAN STARLING

COMMON MYNAH
adult

INDIAN GRACKLE
adult

JAY

MAGPIES AND CROWS

Largest perching birds. Powerful bills. Sexes are alike. Noisy and often gregarious. Attracted by carrion. Intelligent.

TREEPIE *Crypsirina formosae* 灰樹鵲
15" (including 8" tail). Winter visitor (October to April). Distinctive. Note pale grey rump contrasting with dull brown back. Gregarious. An irruption species which is common in some years but absent in others. The last irruption occurred in the 1977/78 winter when one flock numbered over 80 birds. Usually confined to wooded areas, notably the Tai Po Kau Forestry Reserve.

MAGPIE *Pica pica* 喜鵲
18" (including 10" tail). Resident.* Distinctive. Juveniles have a shorter tail. Most familiar call sounds like a bag of coins being shaken. Very common and widespread; found almost everywhere. Conspicuous domed nests are constructed high in trees or pylons. A nest is built every year in the mast on the old Kowloon Railway Station Clock Tower. The breeding season is from December to May and usually six eggs are laid. Magpies are regarded as good luck throughout China.

[AZURE-WINGED MAGPIE *Cyanopica cyanus* 灰喜鵲
not illustrated
13½". Escape. Distinctive jet black head and nape with azure blue wings and tail. Four escaped from the Botanical Gardens at the end of 1975 and are now seen flying free in the area. This species breeds in Central China and it is possible that they may become established in Hong Kong.

BLUE MAGPIE *Urocissa erythrorhyncha* 藍喜鵲
26" (including up to 19" tail). Resident.* Unmistakable. Mostly seen in small parties. Various loud calls and whistles. Quite common and widespread. Found in areas with thick scrub cover. Much more easily seen on Hong Kong Island, particularly Mid-Levels, than in the New Territories where it tends to be local. The nest is a light structure placed in a tree about 20 feet off the ground. The breeding season is April to July, two broods—three to five eggs. Although strikingly attractive they consume large numbers of eggs and fledglings but will not hesitate to tackle a snake. Albinos have been seen twice.

COLLARED CROW *Corvus torquatus* 白頸鴉
20". Local resident.* Distinctive. Common in the Deep Bay area and the eastern New Territories but rare elsewhere although a pair has been present on Stonecutters' Island for some years. Usually recorded near water and often feeds along the shore. Mostly in pairs but gatherings of up to 50 have been met with. Once regarded as common throughout Hong Kong but numbers declined. However, they have recovered in recent years and the population now seems static. A smallish nest is placed in a tree. The breeding season is from December to April.

JUNGLE CROW *Corvus macrorhynchus* 大嘴烏鴉
20". Resident.* Only all-black crow seen in Hong Kong. Powerful bill. Quite common and widespread but absent or scarce in areas where Collared Crow occurs. The population has increased in recent years. Prefers wooded areas but is also met with in large numbers on the mudflats at Tai Po where over 70 have been counted. Nests are of sticks placed high in a tree. The breeding season is from March to June.

TREEPIE

MAGPIE

adult

BLUE MAGPIE

COLLARED CROW

JUNGLE CROW

Lars Phillips

CUCKOO-SHRIKE, MINIVETS AND TITS

BLACK-WINGED CUCKOO-SHRIKE *Coracina melaschistos* 暗灰鵑鵙
9½". Winter visitor* (September to June). At rest, distinctively grey and black with white barred under-tail. Female is duller. Quite common and widespread in recent years. Usually found near trees and often keeps to the canopy, making good observation difficult, except when flying up to catch an insect on the wing. Formerly bred but the only documented record is from Tsuen Wan in July, 1936. 🌲 XXX

MINIVETS

Mostly colourful and active woodland birds, seen moving in small flocks through the canopy. Slender wings with prominent wing bar in flight. Sub-adult males are intermediate in colouration between males and females. Soft musical call notes.

SCARLET MINIVET *Pericrocotus flammeus* 赤紅山椒鳥
8½". Local resident mostly recorded in winter. Distinctive. In spring, young males are orange. Scarlet males number about one in fifteen in winter flocks (Webster). Mostly seen in the Tai Po Kau Forestry Reserve where it is possible that breeding occurred in 1977. Also regularly recorded from the Lam Tsuen Valley and elsewhere in the New Territories but usually in small numbers. 🌲 ⌂

GREY-THROATED MINIVET *Pericrocotus solaris* 灰喉山椒鳥
7½". Occasional winter visitor (November to March). Male separated from similar Scarlet Minivet by smaller size, flame-red colouration (not scarlet), grey throat and sides to head. Females are only separated with difficulty by lack of yellow on forehead and just one wing patch showing on the closed wing. Only seven records, all but one of female/immatures, from widespread wooded areas. 🌲

ASHY MINIVET *Pericrocotus divaricatus* 灰山椒鳥
8". Passage migrant (February to May and September to November). Distinctive. Note white forehead, black crown and nape. On females and immatures these features are not so prominent. Widespread. Found in more open areas than other minivets although usually in the vicinity of trees. Regular in small numbers on the spring passage but scarce in autumn. 🌲 XXX ⌂

TITS

Small, active, short-billed acrobatic birds of wooded areas. Often in loose flocks moving through the canopy. Constantly calling to maintain contact.

GREAT TIT *Parus major* 白臉山雀
5". Resident.* Distinctive but greyer and plainer than the European race. Young birds are yellower than adults. Great variety of calls. A common woodland bird which also regularly visits cultivated land. Although widespread, is surprisingly absent from some apparently suitable areas. Nests in holes in walls and trees. The breeding season is from February to May, two broods—normally six eggs. ■ 🌲 XXX

YELLOW-BELLIED TIT *Parus venustulus* 黃腹山雀
4". Winter visitor (November to April). Separated from Great Tit by much brighter and yellower appearance. Females and immatures have olive green head and upperparts and duller underparts but the general pattern is the same. Voice is a high pitched 'si-si-si-si-si' (Webster). An irruption species which has been recorded in three recent winters (1969/70, 1972, 1976/77), when it was locally common in wooded areas. 🌲

VINOUS-THROATED PARROTBILL *Paradoxornis webbiana* 粉紅鸚嘴
5". Vagrant. Distinctive large head, long tail and parrot-like bill. Three records. The last sighting was of a sizeable flock moving through the undergrowth near Kowloon Reservoirs in spring 1977. Possibly regular but overlooked.

YELLOW-BELLIED TIT

BLACK-WINGED
CUCKOO-SHRIKE

♀

SCARLET MINIVET

♂

GREY-THROATED
MINIVET

♂

VINOUS-THROATED
PARROTBILL

GREAT TIT   adult

♂

ASHY MINIVET

Karen Phillipps

BULBULS

Medium-sized, self confident perching birds. Usually in small parties and quite noisy. Feed on insects, soft berries and fruit. Generally build handsome cup shaped nests which are placed in bushes or trees and lay two to six reddish or pinkish white eggs boldly spotted with red, brown and lilac. Sexes are alike. Mostly non-migratory.

RED-VENTED BULBUL *Pycnonotus aurigaster* 紅屎忽
8″. Resident.* Distinctive whitish patch on upper tail-coverts. Common and widespread but usually found away from built-up areas. Favours scrubland and hillsides. The breeding season is from March to July. The nest is more flimsy than that of other bulbuls and is usually placed high in a tree.

CRESTED BULBUL *Pycnonotus jocosus* 高鶏冠
8″. Resident.* Distinctive. Immatures lack red cheek patch. Cheerful song 'bulbi-bulbit' 'bulbi-bulbit' delivered from high in a tree. Regularly fly-catches from a perch. Pairs often appear affectionate, sitting close together on overhead wires. Common and widespread. Favours parks and gardens as well as quiet woodland. The breeding season is from April to June. Large flocks are occasionally seen outside of the breeding season.

CHINESE BULBUL *Pycnonotus sinensis* 白頭翁
7½″. Resident.* Distinctive. Very young birds lack white head markings and can be confusing. Noisy and less tuneful than Crested Bulbul. Adroit flycatcher from perch. Roosts in considerable numbers, often in mangroves. Large flocks seen in winter. Common and widespread, being found virtually everywhere. The breeding season is from March until August.

CHESTNUT BULBUL *Hypsipetes castanotus* 栗背短脚鵯
8½″. Winter visitor (October to April). Chestnut upperparts, darker head, brown wings and tail are diagnostic. Call 'ting a ling' like a bicycle bell (Webster). An irruption species being quite common in some years with flocks of up to 35 but scarce in others with only odd birds being recorded. Confined to dense thickets and wooded areas. This species breeds nearby in the wooded hills of Fukien and Kwangtung and a midsummer record in the Ho Chung Valley in 1977 suggests that breeding could occur in Hong Kong.

BLACK BULBUL *Hypsipetes madagascariensis* 黑短脚鵯
10″. Winter visitor (November to April). Large size, black plumage, coral red bill and feet are diagnostic. Birds range from entirely black to those with a completely white head and shoulders. Apparently only mature adults have fully white heads although some authorities consider that different races are involved. Immatures can be greyish on the underparts. Long drawn out nasal call resembling a kitten in distress. An irruption species being very common in some years with quite large flocks recorded but scarce or absent in others. The last major irruption occurred in early 1967 when it was evident throughout Hong Kong. In most years a few are recorded in well-wooded areas such as the Tai Po Kau Forestry Reserve.

RED-VENTED BULBUL

CRESTED BULBUL
adult

CHINESE BULBUL
adult

CHESTNUT
BULBUL

BLACK BULBUL

BLACK BULBUL

BABBLERS

Generally skulking, medium-sized birds with longish graduated tails. Poor fliers on short rounded wings. Noisy selection of odd sounds and chatterings usually delivered from the ground or thick undergrowth. More often heard than seen. Insectivorous but also consume fruit and seeds. Sexes are alike. Mostly non-migratory.

WHITE-CHEEKED LAUGHING-THRUSH *Garrulax sannio* 白頰噪鶥
10". Local resident. Distinctively darker crown, buffy white eyebrow and cheek patch. Noisy but more musical than Black-Faced Laughing-Thrush. Not as shy as most babblers and are more active at dawn and dusk. Now locally common and probably breeding where it occurs, although until recently was considered very scarce. Regularly reported from Hong Kong Island, Tseng Lan Shue, Kowloon Reservoirs and even Kowloon Park in the heart of Tsim Sha Tsui. Earlier records were regarded as descendants of escaped birds but it now seems likely that this species has genuinely expanded its range.

BLACK-THROATED LAUGHING-THRUSH *Garrulax chinensis* 黑喉噪鶥
11". Local resident. Distinguished by black throat and white cheeks. Pleasant melodious flute-like call which is repeated rather monotonously. Heard from April until July. Extremely shy, keeping to thick scrub. Virtually confined to Hong Kong Island, particularly Victoria Peak, where it is not uncommon.

HWAMEI *Garrulax canorus* 畫眉
10". Resident.* Conspicuous white eyering and streak behind eye is diagnostic. Strong call and song. Regarded as the characteristic songbird of Chinese avifauna. Shy, although when singing often perches fairly prominently. Common on Hong Kong Island and locally common elsewhere. Once scarce in the New Territories, apparently as a result of illegal trapping, but has increased in recent years. A popular cagebird and considerable numbers are imported. A large shallow nest is constructed close to the ground in a clump of grass or low bush. The breeding season is April to July, at least two broods—three to four eggs. Its common name is Chinese and literally means 'painted eyebrow'

CHINESE BABAX *Babax lanceolatus* 矛紋草鶥
11". Status uncertain.* Up to six were recorded on Tai Mo Shan (above 2000 ft.) between 1959 and 1963 and breeding was proved there in 1960. It is possible that this montane species is still resident as there have been reports of birds there in spring 1977 and on Hong Kong Island in winter 1978.

BLACK-FACED LAUGHING-THRUSH *Garrulax perspicillatus* 七姊妹
12". Resident.* Distinctive broad black mask. Under tail-coverts cinnamon, which are very noticeable in the field. Always in noisy parties of six to twelve clambering about in thickets and undergrowth. Not particularly shy. Strident 'piew' 'piew' 'piew' call. Common and widespread being found anywhere that reasonably thick undergrowth exists. An untidy but well constructed cup shaped nest is built fifteen to twenty feet off the ground in bamboo, shrubs or small trees. The breeding season is March to August and there are usually two broods. Young birds are fed on the wing by the whole party. The Chinese name literally means 'seven sisters.'

GREATER NECKLACED LAUGHING-THRUSH *Garrulax pectoralis* 黑領噪鶥
13". Winter visitor (August to April). Distinctive head pattern and black necklace. Gregarious and parties of up to 40 have been seen. Discovered in 1969 and since then all records have been confined to the Tai Po Kau Forestry Reserve and recently the Shing Mun Plantation. Now probably resident at these localities.

CHINESE BABAX

WHITE-CHEEKED
LAUGHING-THRUSH

BLACK-FACED
LAUGHING-THRUSH

BLACK-THROATED
LAUGHING-THRUSH

HWAMEI

GREATER NECKLACED
LAUGHING-THRUSH

FLYCATCHERS

Small to medium woodland birds with rather flat, broad bills viewed from above. Long bristles at the gape which are usually not visible in the field. Mostly solitary. Insectivorous, catching flies on the wing. Often perch prominently. Males are invariably striking but females are mostly brownish and difficult to separate.

JAPANESE PARADISE FLYCATCHER *Terpsiphone atrocaudata* 紫壽帶鳥
8″ (tail of male up to 9″ more). Passage migrant (April, September and October). As for Asian Paradise Flycatcher but separated by maroon gloss on upperparts. Females have duller heads and are generally browner (not rufous) especially on the tail. Scarce but probably regular in very small numbers.

ASIAN (INCE'S) PARADISE FLYCATCHER *Terpsiphone paradisi* 壽帶鳥
8¾″. (tail of male up to 10″ more). Passage migrant,* but odd birds are recorded throughout the year. Both sexes separated from Japanese Paradise Flycatcher by bright rufous tail and upperparts. Females and some males lack long central tail feathers. Females have a glossy black head but often without a prominent crest. A white form exists but has not been recorded in Hong Kong. Favours well wooded areas. Widespread on passage, particularly September and October, but is never common. One breeding record dated May, 1935.

GREY-HEADED FLYCATCHER *Culicicapa ceylonensis* 方尾鶲
5″. Winter visitor (November to April). Distinctive. Grey head, bright olive brown upperparts and yellow underparts are diagnostic. Constantly uttered call 'silly billy' (Smythies). Bold, friendly, flitting continuously from branch to branch. Nick-named the 'flying banana.' Favours wooded areas, particularly in the Lam Tsuen Valley. Scarce but probably regular in small numbers.

BLACK-NAPED MONARCH FLYCATCHER *Hypothymis azurea* 黑枕王鶲
6½″. Winter visitor (November to April). Distinctive. Long tail sometimes fanned. Not shy. Often noisy, usually utters a harsh chirping. Favours gardens and woodland edges. Widespread and regular in small numbers.

VERDITER FLYCATCHER *Muscicapa thalassina* 銅藍鶲
6⅔″. Winter visitor (October to March). Males wholly greenish blue apart from black lores. Females similar but duller. Perches prominently on tops of trees and overhead wires. Favours wooded areas but sometimes seen in the open. Widespread and regular in small numbers.

HAINAN BLUE FLYCATCHER *Cyornis hainana* 海南藍鶲
6″. Status uncertain.* Male separated from Blue and White Flycatcher by smaller size, lack of white in tail and gradual fading of the dark breast into white underparts. Females are olive brown with chestnut chin and throat. Skulks. Bred at the Tai Po Kau Forestry Reserve from 1963 to 1967 and probably earlier. Otherwise, extremely rare being only once recorded in the last ten years.

BLUE AND WHITE FLYCATCHER *Cyanoptila cyanomelana* 白腹藍鶲
7″. Passage migrant (March to May and September to December). Male separated from Hainan Blue Flycatcher by white bases to outer tail feathers and sharp division between white belly and dark breast. Females are brown with pale throat patch. Males like to be conspicuous and appear large and restless whereas the females are rarely seen. Widespread and probably regular but numbers vary greatly from year to year. Records indicate a recent decline.

[ORANGE-BELLIED NILTAVA *Niltava sundara/davidi* 棕腹大仙鶲
not illustrated
7″. Vagrant (October to December). Male has bright blue upperparts, black throat and orange underparts. Females are generally brownish with white gorget and blue shoulder patch. Four records of three separate males and a female, all from well wooded areas. Two species, inseparable in the field, are involved.]

JAPANESE PARADISE
FLYCATCHER

ASIAN
PARADISE
FLYCATCHER

GREY-HEADED
FLYCATCHER

BLACK-NAPED MONARCH FLYCATCHER

♀

♂

HAINAN
BLUE FLYCATCHER

VERDITER FLYCATCHER

BLUE AND WHITE FLYCATCHER

Kara Phillips

FLYCATCHERS AND SIVA

BROWN FLYCATCHER *Muscicapa latirostris* 闊嘴鶲
$5\frac{1}{4}$''. Winter visitor (September to April). Plainish flycatcher but note whitish eyering, slight pale edging on wings and pale grey breast and flanks Sexes are similar. Mostly silent. Keeps just below the tree canopy; perches quite prominently. Very occasionally on the ground. Commonest flycatcher occurring in Hong Kong. Widespread. Large numbers are sometimes seen on the autumn passage.

GREY-SPOTTED FLYCATCHER *Muscicapa griseisticta* 斑胸鶲
6''. Passage migrant (April, May and September to November). Separated from Brown Flycatcher by conspicuous streaks on breast and flanks. Usually selects a very exposed perch from which to flycatch. Widespread on passage and in some years passes through in quite large numbers.

[**SOOTY FLYCATCHER** *Muscicapa sibirica* 烏鶲
not illustrated
$5\frac{1}{2}$''. Vagrant. Separated from Brown and Grey-Spotted Flycatchers by generally very dark plumage. Underparts are dark grey (actually large blotches) with a white streak down the centre of the throat, breast and belly. Only once recorded (October, 1974) but probably overlooked.

[**FERRUGINOUS FLYCATCHER** *Muscicapa ferruginea* 紅褐鶲
not illustrated
5'' Spring passage migrant (March and April). Dark grey head, rusty upperparts (bright on rump) and bright chestnut-orange on flanks and vent. Centre of underparts and throat are white. Should be quickly recognised by bright rusty rump and tail. Scarce but widespread and possibly regular in very small numbers

RED-BREASTED FLYCATCHER *Ficedula parva* 紅喉鶲
$5\frac{1}{3}$''. Winter visitor (September to May). Often flicks up and spreads blackish tail to show white patches at the base of outer tail feathers. On some birds these white patches are small and difficult to see but the tail is still characteristically flicked. In late spring males have an orange-rufous throat but this is rarely seen in Hong Kong. Calls loudly, sounding like a small wooden rattle rotated at speed (King). Usually keeps near the ground. Widespread. Good numbers pass through in autumn but a few remain and establish winter territories.

ROBIN FLYCATCHER *Ficedula mugimaki* 鴝鶲
$5\frac{1}{4}$''. Winter visitor (October to May). Adult males are distinctive. Females and immatures are olive brown with one or two dull wing bars, buffy rufous throat and breast. Birds of various intermediate plumages are often seen. Usually in small parties and feed either near the ground or in tree-tops. Regular but uncommon, being mostly recorded from the Tai Po Kau Forestry Reserve.

TRICOLOUR FLYCATCHER *Ficedula zanthopygia* 白眉鶲
$5\frac{1}{4}$''. Passage migrant (April, August to October). Separated from Narcissus Flycatcher by white eyebrow. Females are olive with whitish wing bar, golden rump and pale yellow underparts. Widespread but regular in very small numbers in autumn. Rare in spring.

NARCISSUS FLYCATCHER *Ficedula narcissina* 黑背黃眉鶲
$5\frac{1}{4}$''. Spring passage migrant (March to May). Separated from Tricolour Flycatcher by golden eyebrow and usually more orange breast. Female similar to Tricolour Flycatcher but has olive green rump, the same colour as the upperparts. Not shy. Widespread but probably regular in very small numbers.

COLLARED SIVA *Yuhina castaniceps* 栗頭希鶲
$5\frac{1}{2}$''. Winter visitor (November to March). Note short crest, chestnut cheeks with white streaks and white tipped tail. Gregarious, usually in flocks of about thirty. Continually calling 'chir-chit' 'chir-chit'. Usually seen moving through upperparts of trees. In recent years flocks have been regularly seen in well wooded areas such as the Tai Po Kau Forestry Reserve and Shing Mun Plantation.

BROWN
FLYCATCHER

COLLARED SIVA

GREY-SPOTTED
FLYCATCHER

RED-BREASTED
FLYCATCHER
♀

TRICOLOUR
FLYCATCHER
♀

♂

ROBIN
FLYCATCHER

NARCISSUS FLYCATCHER

Karen Phillipps

WARBLERS

Small, plain coloured active birds. Many have distinctive calls. Without experience most are difficult to identify.

GREAT REED WARBLER *Acrocephalus arundinaceus* 大葦鶯
7½". Passage migrant (March to May and August to November). Distinguished by large size, tawny flanks and rump shaded chestnut. Call is a loud harsh 'chack' but frog-like croaking noises are also produced. Found in reed beds and brush usually near water. Very common on the Deep Bay Marshes in autumn but comparatively scarce in spring. Quite regularly seen elsewhere, occasionally in surprising localities. 🐦 ≋

[STYAN'S GRASSHOPPER WARBLER *Locustella pleskei* 伊豆島蝗鶯
not illustrated
6½". Passage migrant. (March to May and September to November). Smaller version of Great Reed Warbler but separated by greyer head, almost pure white throat and pinkish legs. Creeps about mouse-like around base of reeds and on grass banks usually near water. Scarce but probably regular in very small numbers. Mostly recorded on the Deep Bay Marshes. ≋ DB]

VON SCHRENCK'S REED WARBLER *Acrocephalus bistrigiceps* 黑眉葦鶯
5⅓". Passage migrant. (March to May and September to November). Long buffy white eyebrow bordered above and below by dark stripes is diagnostic. Pale chestnut rump. Its melodious but not loud song is heard in April and May. Skulks in reeds and grass, usually near water. Regular on the Deep Bay Marshes, particularly in spring, and occasionally at Kai Tak. ≋ DB

FANTAIL WARBLER *Cisticola juncidis* 棕扇尾鶯
4½". Resident.* Distinguished by small size, pronounced streaks on crown and upperparts, very short tail with subterminal black band and white tips. Readily noticed during high aerial song flight when it utters an insistent 'chip, chip, chip,' Skulks in reeds and grass but is restless and often flushed from one grass clump to the next. Although known to have bred in summer on the Deep Bay Marshes is most often seen in winter. Found in grassland and paddy areas throughout the New Territories. 🐦 ♣ ≋

[PALLAS'S GRASSHOPPER WARBLER *Locustella certhiola* 小蝗鶯
not illustrated
6". Winter visitor (September to May). Similar to Fantail Warbler but distinguished by larger size, longer tail and fainter streaking on crown. Secretive, keeping close to the ground. Found in reeds, thickets and grass near water. Scarce, but probably regular in very small numbers to the Deep Bay area. ≋ DB]

DUSKY WARBLER *Phylloscopus fuscatus* 褐柳鶯
5". Winter visitor (September to May). Rather nondescript but often has a rusty tinge to flanks and abdomen. Call is a harsh 'tschack-tschack.' Moves methodically through bushes, reeds and mangroves, although it keeps concealed. Can be located by its call and with patience be well seen. Common and widespread. ♠ ✕✕✕ 🐦 ≋ 🌙

YELLOW-BELLIED WREN-WARBLER *Prinia flaviventris* 灰頭鷦鶯
5½". Resident.* Separated from Brown Wren-Warbler by slaty grey head, olive green upperparts and yellow belly contrasting with white or creamy buff throat. Immatures have the upperparts brownish. Weak top heavy flight. A curious clicking sound is made in flight. Shy, except when singing its short rollicking song from an exposed perch. Also produces a cat like 'mew.' Common and widespread, occurs wherever reeds or a stand of tall grass are found. The nest is oval shaped, usually placed in a small bush. The breeding season is from May to August, up to three broods. ♠ ✕✕✕ 🐦 ♣ ≋ 🌙

BROWN WREN-WARBLER *Prinia subflava* 褐頭鷦鶯
6". Local resident.* Best separated from immature Yellow-Bellied Wren-Warblers by long tail and white eyebrow extending beyond the eye. Call is a fairly staccato 'chip' or 'chip-up,' repeated many times. Weak top heavy flight. Apparently restricted to reed beds on the Deep Bay Marshes where it is common and found throughout the year. The nest is purse shaped, attached to reed stems. The breeding season is from May to August. ≋ DB

[DAVID'S HILL-WARBLER *Prinia polychroa* 褐山鷦鶯
not illustrated
7". Local resident. Distinguished from other wren-warblers by large size, dark plumage, streaking on upperparts, fulvous flanks and vent and barring on sides of breast in spring. Confined to the upper slopes of Tai Mo Shan (above 2500 ft). First discovered 1957 after which it was seen regularly until 1966. Rediscovered in spring 1975. ♣]

GREAT REED WARBLER

VON SCHRENCK'S
REED WARBLER

FANTAIL WARBLER

DUSKY WARBLER

adult

YELLOW-BELLIED
WREN-WARBLER

BROWN WREN-WARBLER

Karen Phillipps

WARBLERS AND WHITE-EYES

CHINESE BUSH WARBLER   *Cettia diphone*   短翅樹鶯
Male 7", Female 6". Winter visitor. (September to April). Separated from similar Great Reed Warbler by dull rufous crown and small white area on shoulder of closed wing. Keeps to thick undergrowth and bushes. Churring alarm calls. Pleasant spring song 'kolo-olo-olo-wichit-chit.' Widespread and fairly common.

LONG-TAILED TAILOR-BIRD   *Orthotomus sutorius*   裁縫鳥
4¾" (male tail up to 1½" longer in breeding season). Resident.* Distinctive rufous forehead and crown and very long tail (often cocked). Variety of calls and songs. Common and widespread. Keeps to undergrowth and often difficult to see well but is not shy. Constructs unique nest; the edges of one or two leaves are stitched together to form a firm support for the small round nest which is built in the cup of leaves, usually placed within a few feet of the ground. The breeding season is from April to August, three or four eggs.

YELLOW-BROWED WARBLER   *Phylloscopus inornatus*   黃眉柳鶯
4½". Winter visitor (September to April). Separated by double yellowish white wing bars and patterned tertials. Occasionally has faint coronal streak. Call is a plaintive 'weest.' Very active; mostly in the upper branches of trees. Common and widespread.

PALLAS'S WARBLER   *Phylloscopus proregulus*   黃腰柳鶯
4". Winter visitor (November to April). Distinguished by bright yellow rump, coronal stripe, eyebrow and double wing bars. The similar Yellow-Browed Warbler lacks the yellow rump and is not as brightly coloured. Often hovers. Sometimes in small parties. Very active, found mostly in wooded areas. Usually common and widespread but scarce in some years.

ARCTIC WARBLER   *Phylloscopus borealis*   極北柳鶯
5". Passage migrant (March to May and September to November). Separated with difficulty from Yellow-Browed Warbler by longer, thinner appearance and indistinct wing bar (occasionally two). Call is a loud 'tzick.' Found in bushes and shrubs in quite open areas as well as woodland. Quite common and widespread in autumn but scarce in spring.

[PALE-LEGGED WILLOW-WARBLER   *Phylloscopus tenellipes*   灰腳柳鶯
not illustrated
5". Winter visitor (September to April). Olive brown upperparts, darker on the crown and golden brown on the rump. Prominent white eyebrow. Double indistinct wing bars. Underparts white washed brown on sides of breast and flanks. Vent buffish-yellow. Keeps to undergrowth and lower branches of trees. Call-note is a distinct metallic 'tik-tik.' Widespread but scarce; probably regular in small numbers.   ♣]

[CROWNED WILLOW-WARBLER   *Phylloscopus coronatus*   冕柳鶯
not illustrated
5". Winter visitor (October to March). As other warblers but has pale olive coronal stripe and lemon yellow under tail-coverts. One distinct wing bar (occasionally a faint second bar). Found in open wooded areas. Widespread; probably regular in very small numbers.   ♣]

SHORT-TAILED BUSH WARBLER   *Cettia squameiceps*   鱗頭樹鶯
4½". Winter visitor (October to April). Identified by short tail, broad black eye-stripe and long buffy eyebrow. Stays on or near ground in undergrowth. Voice is a soft 'chip' 'chip.' Not uncommon in well wooded areas; particularly favours the Tai Po Kau Forestry Reserve.

WHITE-EYE   *Zosterops japonica*   相思雀
4¾". Resident.* Conspicuous eyering. Gregarious, often in large flocks in winter. Call-note is like the sound of a silver bell (Herklots). Found in differing habitats, from coastal mangrove to dense woodland. Common, particularly in winter. The nest is a well constructed cup of grass slung inside the fork of a twig or attached to one side of it. The breeding season is from March to August, several broods – three or four eggs. A very popular cagebird and persistent illegal trapping appears to have had no effect on its numbers. Occasionally orange-headed varieties are reported, but this colouration is due to pollen collected by the birds when taking nectar.

[CHESTNUT-FLANKED WHITE-EYE   *Zosterops erythropleura*   紅脇綉眼鳥
not illustrated.
4¾". Vagrant. As White-Eye but with bright chestnut flanks. One record from Hong Kong Island. Possibly overlooked as it could occur regularly.   ]

CHINESE BUSH WARBLER

LONG-TAILED TAILOR-BIRD

YELLOW-BROWED WARBLER

ARCTIC WARBLER

PALLAS'S WARBLER

WHITE-EYE

SHORT-TAILED BUSH WARBLER

Karen Phillipp

ROBINS

Small to medium birds generally keeping to undergrowth. Insectivorous. Tail often cocked.

BLUETHROAT *Erithacus svecica* 藍點頦
6″. Winter visitor (October to April). Winter male resembles female. Both sexes have rufous base to outer tail feathers which is conspicuous in flight. Secretive; keeps to dense cover usually near water. Regular in small numbers but confined to the Deep Bay area and Long Valley. Mostly single birds but parties of up to five have been recorded.

RUBYTHROAT *Erithacus calliope* 紅點頦
6½″. Winter visitor (September to April). Adult male unmistakable. Females and immatures lack red throat but are rarely recorded. Call is a plaintive whistle. Skulks and is difficult to flush. Heard far more often than seen. Keeps to thick undergrowth but occasionally in the open when it does not appear shy. Widespread. Trapping during the 1965/66 winter confirmed that it is present in large numbers.

RED-FLANKED BLUETAIL *Tarsiger cyanurus* 紅脇藍尾鴝
6″. Winter visitor (November to April). Both sexes have rufous-orange flanks and blue tails. Call is a quiet 'chack' 'chack.' Upright and flycatcher-like in appearance. Behaviour is reminiscent of an English Robin. Particularly favours woodland clearings. In Hong Kong females and immatures outnumber males by at least ten to one. Widespread and usually common but numbers vary and in some years it is scarce or absent.

[PALLAS'S BLUE ROBIN *Erithacus cyane* 藍歌鴝
not illustrated
5¾″. Vagrant. Male has white underparts and dark blue upperparts with a broad black streak from bill to sides of breast. Female has olive brown upperparts (without any rufous) and whitish underparts with brown scales on the breast. A male (quite wild) was seen in the Botanical Gardens in April 1973.　　　　　　]

RED-TAILED ROBIN *Erithacus sibilans* 紅尾歌鴝
5½″. Winter visitor (October to April). Diagnostic olive brown crescent-shaped scales on throat, breast and flanks and dark rufous tail. Shivers tail. Keeps to undergrowth. Widespread. Scarce but regular in small numbers.

[JAPANESE ROBIN *Erithacus akahige* 日本歌鴝
not illustrated
6″. Vagrant (January to March). Male has rufous-orange throat, upper breast, forehead and sides of neck, black breast band, grey flanks and white abdomen. Upperparts are dark rufous-brown with chestnut tail. Females are duller and lack breast band. Skulks, keeping to woodland undergrowth. Twice recorded from well-wooded areas. This species is migratory and because of its secretive habits may be overlooked.　　]

MAGPIE-ROBIN *Copsychus saularis* 豬屎喳
8¼″. Resident.* Unmistakable pied plumage. Often cocks tail. Loud, varied melodious song. Quite common and widespread. Usually found near habitation. Fond of feeding in the open, particularly on lawns. Not so commonly recorded away from civilisation but found in coastal mangroves. Strongly territorial and well known for striking its own reflection. A hole nesting species which will construct a nest almost anywhere. The breeding season is March to July, two or three broods – two to five eggs. A popular cagebird.

BLUETHROAT

RUBYTHROAT ♂

BLUETHROAT
(Breeding)

RED-FLANKED
BLUETAIL

♂

♀

MAGPIE-ROBIN

RED-TAILED ROBIN

♀

♂

Karen Phillips

CHATS, REDSTARTS AND DIPPER

GREY BUSHCHAT *Saxicola ferrea* 灰林鵙
6". Winter visitor (October to April). Male distinctively grey. Females are quite unlike males and are brownish with chestnut rump and tail. Usually in pairs or small parties. Often perch on low bushes in clearings. Uncommon but regular in small numbers, returning annually to favoured localities. The Lam Tsuen Valley and the Sai Kung area are good places to look for this species. Not usually seen before December.　　〤〤 ⌂

DAURIAN REDSTART *Phoenicurus auroreus* 灰頂紅尾鴝
6". Winter visitor (September to April). Both sexes have diagnostic white wing patches, rufous rump and tail. Often perches quite prominently. Shivers tail. Found both at woodland edges and in open country. Quite common and widespread.　　🌲 〤〤 ⌂

STONECHAT *Saxicola torquata* 黑喉石鵙
5½". Winter visitor (August to April). Adult male unmistakable. Most birds seen in Hong Kong are immatures and females which are very variable. However, most show white wing patches in flight. Plump and upright, always seen prominently perched on bush-tops, fences or overhead wires. They enjoy being seen. Restless, continually flicking wings and spreading their tails. Common and widespread; favour open cultivated areas, lowland scrubland and reed beds.　　〤〤 ⌂ ≋

PLUMBEOUS WATER-REDSTART *Rhyacornis fuliginosus* 紅尾水鴝
5½". Winter visitor (October to April). Males are unmistakable but scarce in full plumage. White and black tail of females and immatures is always prominently displayed. Perches on rocks in streams and flicks tail repeatedly. Uncommon but regular in small numbers to mountain streams. Good areas to find this species are the headwaters of Tai Lam Chung Reservoir, Ho Chung Valley and Brides Pool above Plover Cove Reservoir.　　≋

[**WHITE-CAPPED REDSTART** *Thamnolaea leucocephalus* 白頂溪鴝
not illustrated
7½". Vagrant. Striking white crown, rest of head, breast and wings black contrasting with deep rich orange of underparts, rump and tail. Black tip to tail. Frequents mountain streams. One remained at Brides Pool above Plover Cove Reservoir from February to April 1974.　　≋]

BROWN DIPPER *Cinclus pallasii* 褐河烏
8½". Vagrant. Large size and chocolate brown appearance is diagnostic. Frequents mountain streams. Two records of single birds in the Lam Tsuen Valley and on Sunset Peak, Lantau. Hong Kong is within this species' range and it could be resident on suitable streams in the remotest areas of the New Territories. ≋

[**PIED BUSHCHAT** *Saxicola caprata* 白斑黑石鵙
not illustrated.
5½". Vagrant. Male is unmistakable, resembling a Stonechat in behaviour but is all black except for white rump, under tail-coverts and patches in wings. Females and immatures separated from similar chats only with difficulty. Single males have been reported from Kai Tak and Victoria Barracks on several occasions in 1976 and 1977. It is likely that these birds have been accidentally introduced, although Hong Kong is not far from this species' known range.　　🏠 ⚹]

GREY BUSHCHAT
♀

DAURIAN REDSTART
♂
♀

STONECHAT

GREY BUSHCHAT
♂

♀

STONECHAT
♂

PLUMBEOUS
WATER-REDSTART
♂

♀

BROWN DIPPER

Karen Phillipps

THRUSHES

Medium to large ground feeding birds having thin bills and square tails. Plumage of females and immatures differs from males and are often difficult to specifically identify. Mostly shy woodland birds. Migratory.

BLUE ROCK-THRUSH *Monticola solitaria* 藍磯鶇
9″. Non-breeding visitor. Two races occur with males ranging from all blue (race *pandoo*) to blue with chestnut-rufous belly (race *philippensis*). Intermediate forms are regularly seen. Most records are of females or immatures. Flicks tail constantly. Adopts an upright posture and is often seen sitting on an exposed rock or corner of a building. Quite common from September to March, being found in a wide variety of habitats from rocky shores to bare hillsides and even urban areas. Once or twice recorded singing in spring and summer on the summit of Tai Mo Shan.

CHESTNUT-BREASTED ROCK-THRUSH *Monticola rufiventris* 栗胸磯鶇
9½″. Winter visitor (November to April). Male separated from Blue Rock-Thrush (red-bellied form) by brighter blue upperparts and chestnut underparts extending to the upper breast. Females are similar but separated by broad whitish streak on centre of throat and lack of blue in plumage. Probably regular in very small numbers, particularly on Hong Kong Island. Found generally in the same areas as Blue Rock-Thrush.

PALE THRUSH *Turdus pallidus* 白腹鶇
11½″. Winter visitor (November to April). In flight broad white tips to outer tail feathers are distinctive. Females and immatures similar but head, neck and breast are browner, throat white with some streaking. Alarm note uttered when flushed. Widespread. Numbers vary from year to year and, although regular, is generally scarce.

EYE-BROWED THRUSH *Turdus obscurus* 白眉鶇
9″. Winter visitor (November to May). Both sexes have distinctive eyebrow. Females are duller with an olive brown head and white throat streaked brown. Very shy. Sometimes in parties, which when alarmed fly to the highest tree-top. Widespread. Scarce but probably regular in small numbers. Mostly recorded in March and April.

BROWN THRUSH *Turdus chrysolaus* 赤腹鶇
11½″. Winter visitor (December to March). Lack of eyebrow separates this species from Eye-Browed Thrush. Females are duller with streaked whitish throat. Very scarce but probably regular in small numbers.

VIOLET WHISTLING THRUSH *Myiophoneus caeruleus* 紫嘯鶇
13″. Resident.* In good light the violet plumage with lighter spangles is unmistakable. Fans tail. Penetrating low whistle. Frequents streams in wooded areas. Locally common, particularly on the northern slopes of Hong Kong Island. A cup shaped nest is constructed, usually on a ledge near a stream but occasionally in a tree. The breeding season is April to June, up to three broods – three or four eggs.

BLUE ROCK-THRUSH
♂

BLUE ROCK-THRUSH
(Red-Bellied)
♂

BLUE
ROCK-THRUSH
♀

CHESTNUT-BREASTED
ROCK-THRUSH
♂

PALE THRUSH

EYE-BROWED THRUSH

VIOLET WHISTLING
THRUSH

BROWN THRUSH

Karen Phillipps

THRUSHES

DUSKY THRUSH *Turdus naumanni* 斑鶇
10″. Winter visitor (December to April). Two distinct races occur. The dark race (*eunomus*) accounts for virtually all records; the red-tailed race (*naumanni*) having only been seen on very few occasions. Intermediates could occur. Females and immatures are similar but show less chestnut. Favours open grassland and playing fields and is therefore easier to see than most thrushes. An irruption species, being common in some years and totally absent in others.　　　　　　　　　　　　　　　　　　　　　🕊 XXX ♣

GREY-BACKED THRUSH *Turdus hortulorum* 灰背鶇
10″. Winter visitor (November to April). Grey upperparts of male are distinctive. Keeps close to the ground and spends much time turning over leaf litter. Normally hops away when disturbed. A garden and woodland thrush. Widespread and quite common in some years.　　　　　　　　　　　　　　　　　🕊 🌲

GREY THRUSH *Turdus cardis* 烏灰鶇
8½″. Winter visitor (November to April). Male distinctive. Female is difficult to separate from similar Grey-Backed Thrush, but is smaller and generally has less orange and more spots on the flanks. A woodland thrush. Widespread. Scarce but regular in small numbers.　　　　　　　　　　　　　　　　🌲

BLACKBIRD *Turdus merula* 烏鶇
11″. Winter visitor (November to March). Distinctive all black male with yellow bill. Female is dark brown with some indistinct streaking. As the familiar Blackbird of Europe but in Hong Kong is much shyer. Its song is never heard but noisy calls and alarm notes are. Usually in small flocks, frequently keeping to tree-tops. Widespread but uncommon. The Lam Tsuen Valley in February is a good place to look for this species.　　　　　　　　　　　　　　　　　　　　　　　　　　　　　　🕊 🌲 XXX

[**SIBERIAN THRUSH** *Zoothera sibiricus* 白眉地鶇
not illustrated
9½″. Occasional winter visitor (November to May). Male slaty black with prominent white eye-stripe. Female has buffy eye-stripe and distinctive dark brown barring on underparts. All records are of single males, seen on seven occasions, mostly on Hong Kong Island.　　　　　　　　　　　　　　　　🌲]

WHITE'S THRUSH *Zoothera dauma* 虎斑山鶇
11″. Winter visitor (November to April). Unmistakable. Flight is rapid and undulating; black and white bands show on the underwing. Found both in woodland and more open areas. Widespread. Numbers vary from year to year but is generally scarce.　　　　　　　　　　　　　　　　🌲 XXX ⌂

ORANGE-HEADED GROUND-THRUSH *Zoothera citrinus* 橙頭地鶇
8½″. Occasional winter visitor (October to April). Male is unmistakable. Females and immatures are similar but upperparts are olive brown. A garden and woodland thrush. Odd birds have been recorded in six winters in recent years. Some have remained in the same locality for four or five months.　　　　　🕊 🌲

DUSKY THRUSH

GREY-BACKED THRUSH

DUSKY THRUSH
(Red-Tailed)

GREY THRUSH

BLACKBIRD

WHITE'S THRUSH

ORANGE-HEADED
GROUND-THRUSH

Karen Phillipps

PIPITS AND SKYLARK

PIPITS
Small to medium dull brownish birds with varying amounts of streaking and white outer tail feathers. Slender. Undulating flight. Difficult to identify but distinctive calls help. Insectivorous, food is taken mostly on the ground.

RICHARD'S PIPIT (CHINESE PIPIT) *Anthus novaeseelandiae* 田鷚
6–8″. Winter and summer visitor.* Separated by long-legged erect stance and band of narrow blackish streaks confined to the breast. Long hind claw is often noticeable when perched on overhead wires. Harsh call note. Usually found singly in open country, particularly grassy areas and paddy stubble. Widespread and common in winter. Much scarcer in summer when the wintering race (*richardi*) is replaced by a smaller and darker race (*sinensis*) called the Chinese Pipit. The latter race is known to have bred in a number of localities throughout Hong Kong.

INDIAN TREE PIPIT (OLIVE-BACKED PIPIT) *Anthus hodgsoni* 樹鷚
6½″. Winter visitor (October to April). Separated by strikingly olive-green upperparts. Wags tail more than other pipits. Call is a quiet 'tseep.' Found both in cultivated areas and woodland. Flies up to overhead wires but more often trees when flushed. Usually in small parties. Common and widespread.

RED-THROATED PIPIT *Anthus cervinus* 紅喉鷚
6½″. Winter visitor (October to April). Reddish throat in breeding plumage is unmistakable. In other plumages separated from Indian Tree Pipit by bold blackish streaks on brownish upperparts. Call is similar to Indian Tree Pipit. Favours damp areas but also found on cultivated land. Fairly common in the northern New Territories and local elsewhere. The marshy areas either side of Lok Ma Chau Road hold good numbers of these pipits in spring.

WATER PIPIT *Anthus spinoletta* 水鷚
6½″. Occasional winter visitor (October to March). Generally darker and greyer than other pipits. Call note is a sharp double 'tsupi' often repeated several times when flushed. Wary and when alarmed rises to a considerable height. Found in marshy areas. Irregularly recorded in recent years but in two winters in the late nineteen-fifties was considered common on the Deep Bay Marshes – perhaps erroneously.

UPLAND PIPIT *Anthus sylvanus* 山鷚
7″. Local resident*. Only safely separable in the field from Richard's Pipit by its unusual song – 'weeeeeeeee tch weeeeeeeee tch' (Murton), which carries very far. The bill is heavier and the underparts tend to be spotted rather than streaked. Low darting flight when flushed. Found on most upland above 1500 ft. Good areas to find this species are Tai Mo Shan, Ma On Shan, Kowloon Peak and Sunset Peak on Lantau. A well built bulky nest is constructed on the ground amongst grass tussocks. The breeding season is March to August and three to five eggs are laid.

SMALL SKYLARK *Alauda gulgula* 小雲雀
6½″. Resident.* Separated from pipits by heavier (less slender) bill, short crest (often difficult to see), fluttery weak flight and thin whitish trailing edge to wings. When disturbed crouches rather than runs. Call is a liquid 'chirrup.' Found locally on open grassy areas and overgrown reclaimed land. Mostly recorded from Kai Tak where it is present in good numbers in winter. Breeding was proved there in 1974 and 1975.

102

SMALL SKYLARK

RICHARD'S PIPIT

INDIAN TREE PIPIT

RED-THROATED PIPIT

WATER PIPIT

UPLAND PIPIT

WAGTAILS

Small to medium, slender long-tailed birds with striking plumage patterns. Wag tails constantly. Strong bounding flight. Mostly on the ground. Closely related to pipits.

YELLOW WAGTAIL   *Motacilla flava*   黃鶺鴒
7". Winter visitor (August to May). Variable but olive green upperparts always separates this species from Grey Wagtail. At least three distinct races are regular. The commonest (*taivana*) occurs throughout the winter but the other two, the Blue-Headed Wagtail (*simillina*) and the Grey-Headed Wagtail (*macronyx*), are passage migrants. Immatures are brownish above with white eyebrow, underparts white with (but not always) yellowish wash. Call is a wheezy 'tsreep' when flushed and flying. Found mostly in damp areas, particularly in the Deep Bay area, but also regularly on cultivated land. Roosts in large numbers in reed beds and mangroves.

FOREST WAGTAIL   *Dendronanthus indicus*   林鶺鴒
7". Passage migrant (April, September and October). Recognised by black breast markings and large whitish wing bars. Sways body and tail from side to side. Often perches in trees. Found mostly in woodland but also occasionally gardens. Regular in small numbers in autumn but scarce in spring. Widespread.

WHITE WAGTAIL   *Motacilla alba*   白鶺鴒
7½". Winter visitor (August to May). Variable but pied plumage is distinctive. Two races occur: Streak-Eyed (*ocularis*) and White-Faced (*leucopsis*). Both races are common but Streak-Eyed is probably more numerous. The call is a hard 'chissick' uttered in flight. During winter evenings huge numbers roost in and around Statue Square and on the roof of the Supreme Court. In the past breeding at Kai Tak has been suspected but never proved.

GREY WAGTAIL   *Motacilla cinerea*   灰鶺鴒
7½". Winter visitor (August to May). Separated from Yellow Wagtail by grey upperparts. In summer, throat of male is black. Immatures whiter on underparts but always yellow under the tail. Throat is never yellow. Call is a clear, sharp 'chitik', harsher than White Wagtail. Found mostly near streams and water catchments but also in open cultivated country. Widespread and common. Large numbers pass through in autumn.

CITRINE WAGTAIL   *Motacilla citreola*   黃頭鶺鴒
7". Vagrant. Bright yellow head of summer male is diagnostic. Winter adults and summer females similar to Yellow Wagtail but distinguished by two thinnish white wing bars (particularly noticeable in flight) and yellow forehead. Immatures are not safely separable. One record of a summer male at Mai Po on 11 September 1973. Probably overlooked as only a small percentage are likely to be males in breeding plumage.

≋DB

YELLOW WAGTAIL
(Blue-Headed)

FOREST WAGTAIL

WHITE WAGTAIL
(White-Faced)

adult

GREY WAGTAIL
non-breeding

CITRINE WAGTAIL
breeding

YELLOW WAGTAIL

Karou Phillipp

SUNBIRD, FLOWERPECKERS AND PEKIN ROBIN

FORK-TAILED SUNBIRD *Aethopyga christinae* 叉尾太陽鳥
4''. (male tail up to $\frac{3}{4}$'' more). Resident. Identified by distinctive decurved bill. Immatures and females are much duller being generally greenish, yellower below. Call of male is a loud metallic 'chiff-chiff-chiff.' Sunbirds are the Old World equivalent of humming-birds. They dart from flower to flower and although capable of hovering, prefer to perch beside the flower, performing considerable acrobatic movements to obtain the nectar. First discovered in the Tai Po Kau Forestry Reserve in June, 1959, when a pair were seen with two young. Sunbirds have since been regularly seen in several localities on Hong Kong Island, Lam Tsuen Valley, Ho Chung and the Sai Kung area. Likely to be found in any garden or woodland where good numbers of flowering bushes and trees occur. The breeding season is May and June and the nest is a ball of grass placed in a tree, usually about ten feet off the ground.

FLOWERPECKERS
Minute birds with short bills and tails. The males are brilliantly coloured. Highly active with a darting, somewhat erratic flight. Difficult to see as they feed in the tops of flowering trees and often only their sharp metallic 'chip chip chip' call is heard as they bound away to another tree.

FIRE-BREASTED FLOWERPECKER *Dicaeum ignipectus* 紅胸啄花雀
$3\frac{1}{2}$''. Status uncertain (September to June). Male is striking but black belly stripe is particularly noticeable. Female is similar to immature Scarlet-Backed Flowerpecker but has bright buffy underparts. Song is a strident 'see-bit' 'seé-bit' 'see-bit' 'see-bit.' Scarce, being mostly recorded between November and February but recent sightings in June suggest that it may be resident. Widespread but most often seen in the Tai Po Kau Forestry Reserve.

SCARLET-BACKED FLOWERPECKER *Dicaeum cruentatum* 朱背啄花雀
$3\frac{1}{2}$'' Resident.* Both sexes have scarlet on the upperparts. Immatures lack scarlet but often have dull orange tinge to rump, which is difficult to see. Locally common; regularly recorded on Hong Kong Island, the Tai Po Kau Forestry Reserve and the Lam Tsuen Valley. A pear shaped nest is placed near the end of a high branch. The breeding season is June to August.

PEKIN ROBIN *Leiothrix lutea* 紅嘴相思鳥
6''. Status uncertain. Females have paler throat and breast and lack red in primaries. Normally a bird of woodland undergrowth in montane areas. Fairly frequently recorded from widespread localities. However as this is a popular cagebird most occurences are suspected to be escapes. Nevertheless, a review of records suggests that a few sightings between December and May in well-wooded areas, such as the Tai Po Kau Forestry Reserve, are of genuinely wild birds.

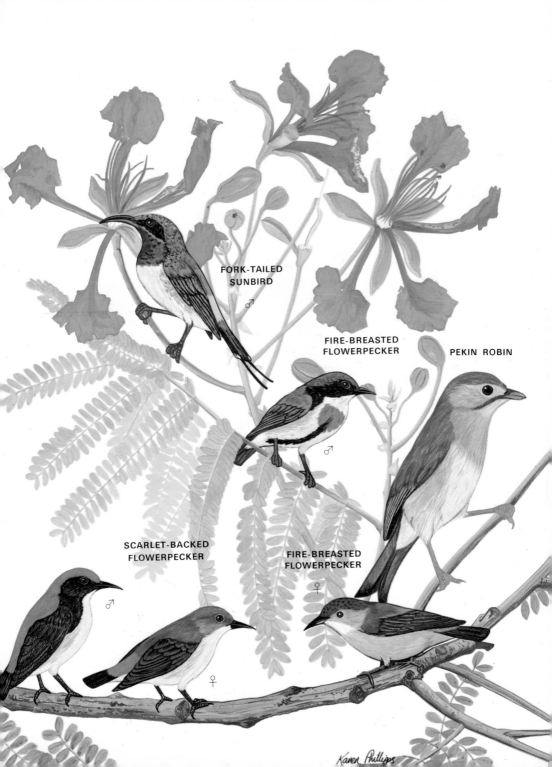

FORK-TAILED
SUNBIRD

♂

FIRE-BREASTED
FLOWERPECKER

PEKIN ROBIN

♂

SCARLET-BACKED
FLOWERPECKER

FIRE-BREASTED
FLOWERPECKER

♂

♀

♀

Karen Phillips

FINCHES

Small to medium birds with compact, conical seed-eating bills, rounded wings and notched tails. Males are often more colourful. Undulating flight. Gregarious outside the breeding season.

CHINESE GREENFINCH *Carduelis sinica* 金翅雀
5½". Resident.* Adult male unmistakable. Females and immatures are paler and generally browner but still have distinctive yellow wing bars. Constant quiet trilling call. In winter, usually seen in flocks of up to 150. Locally common. The nest is a deep cup about four inches across with thick walls, constructed in a bush or tree. The breeding season starts as early as January and continues until June. The usual clutch is four eggs. Formerly nested in the large Banyans (*Ficus retusa*) along Nathan Road, Kowloon.

SISKIN *Carduelis spinus* 黃雀
4¾". Vagrant. Small yellowish green, dark streaked finch with yellow rump. Females lack black cap and are more streaked. At least one flock of up to 30 was in the Tai Po Kau Forestry Reserve during January and February 1973. Other records are of single birds and it is likely that these were escapes as this is a popular cagebird. However, the flock seen in 1973 undoubtedly comprised wild birds and it seems probable that this is an irruption species.

[**YELLOW-FRONTED CANARY** *Serinus mozambicus*
not illustrated
6". Escape. A very common cagebird which originates from East Africa and superficially resembles a Siskin but lacks black markings and streaks. Single escapes are occasionally met with, particularly on Hong Kong Island.
]

COMMON ROSEFINCH *Carpodacus erythrinus* 朱雀
6½". Winter visitor (October to April). Male unmistakable but the extent of red is variable. Females and immatures are nondescript, but are the only streaked brown finches occurring in Hong Kong – note the pale double wing bar. Generally seen in small flocks of females and immatures but often the presence of an adult male eases identification. Widespread and regular in small numbers. Prefers scrubland areas along margins of woods and cultivation. Good areas to find this species are the Lam Tsuen Valley, Sai Kung, Shek Kong and the Mong Tseng Peninsula.

BLACK-TAILED HAWFINCH *Coccothraustes migratoria* 黑尾蠟咀雀
8". Winter visitor (November to April). Distinctive massive triangular yellow bill and forked tail. Female similar but the head is grey-brown, throat and central tail feathers are grey. Usually in flocks of up to 40. Locally common in the New Territories but scarce on Hong Kong Island. Occurs in much the same areas as Common Rosefinch but generally prefers more open country.

[**BRAMBLING** *Fringilla montifringilla* 花雀
not illustrated
6". Vagrant (December). Blackish or brownish head, neck, wings and back, conspicuous white rump and belly, reddish-brown on breast and flanks. Females are duller and browner. Feeds mostly on the ground. Only two records but it seems probable that this is an irruption species, particularly during hard weather.
]

JAVA SPARROW *Padda oryzivora* 禾谷
6⅓". Introduced. Adult unmistakable. Immatures tinged browner. Gregarious. Recorded almost annually in small numbers but a flock of 150 was seen in early 1967. A common cagebird which would not occur here normally. Often used by Chinese fortune-tellers. Breeding, although suspected, has not been proved. In recent years quite regularly seen in the Sai Kung area.

TREE SPARROW *Passer montanus* 麻雀
5¾". Resident.* The familiar sparrow of urban areas. Occurs commonly around dwelling-houses but is absent on some sparsely populated outlying islands. Occasionally large flocks of several hundred are met with around grain wharves and in fields of uncut rice, but generally not far from habitation. The nest is a large untidy ball of grass usually placed in a hole or crevice of a building. The breeding season is from March to August; at least three broods – four or five eggs. This species replaces the English House Sparrow (*Passer domesticus*) in the Far East.

CHINESE GREENFINCH

SISKIN

COMMON ROSEFINCH

♀

♂

JAVA SPARROW

adult

BLACK-TAILED HAWFINCH

TREE SPARROW

BUNTINGS

Similar to finches. Most skulk and keep to undergrowth. Breeding males are distinctive but other plumages are much duller and specific identification is often difficult.

TRISTRAM'S BUNTING *Emberiza tristrami* 白鵰鵐
6". Winter visitor (November to March) All plumages have prominent head stripes. Females and immatures are not so well marked. The rump and upper tail-coverts are chestnut. Call is a soft 'chip.' Keeps to woodland undergrowth. Regular in good numbers at the Tai Po Kau Forestry Reserve but scarce elsewhere.

MASKED BUNTING *Emberiza spodocephala* 灰頭鵐
6". Winter visitor (October to May). Plumage variable. Females and immatures are often nondescript and can only be recognised by the absence of any striking field characteristic. When agitated the crown feathers are often slightly raised suggesting a crest. Continually twitches tail revealing white outer tail feathers. Call is a quiet 'tsic' 'tsic' – a familiar sound in winter emanating from thick undergrowth. Easily Hong Kong's commonest bunting, occurring in any open areas which have suitable cover.

GREY-HEADED BUNTING *Emberiza fucata* 赤胸鵐
6⅓". Winter visitor (November to April). In all plumages has chestnut cheeks and shoulders and black moustache stripe running down into a necklace of broad black streaks on the upper breast. Winter males and females lack chestnut breast band and the head and nape is browner. Keeps to open and usually marshy areas. Formerly considered common and widespread but now only regular in small numbers to the northern New Territories. Long Valley and the Mong Tseng Peninsula are good districts to look for this species.

YELLOW-BREASTED BUNTING *Emberiza aureola* 黃胸鵐
6". Passage migrant (September to April). Both sexes have white wing patches but these are much less prominent in females and immatures. Gregarious. Found in open areas, particularly rice-fields and reed beds Numbers vary from year to year but is often common in autumn. Winter records are few and is scarce in spring. Immense flocks descend on the rice-fields of China in autumn and must do considerable damage to the crop. This is the 'rice-bird' much prized in Cantonese cuisine.

CHESTNUT BUNTING *Emberiza rutila* 栗鵐
5¾". Passage migrant (October to December, March and April). The only bunting not to show prominent white tail feathers in flight. Dull chestnut rump is a good field mark. Widespread but only regular in very small numbers. Females and immatures are probably overlooked. Favours woodland edges and occasionally cultivated areas.

LITTLE BUNTING *Emberiza pusilla* 小鵐
5". Winter visitor (October to April). All plumages show chestnut cheek and head stripe but is less prominent on females and immatures. Found in any open areas, but particularly favours reed beds. Widespread. Formerly regarded as common but in recent years has been rather scarce. Can usually be found at Mai Po, particularly during the early spring migration.

[**RUSTIC BUNTING** *Emberiza rustica* 田鵐
not illustrated
5¾". Vagrant. Breeding male has distinctive black head with white streak running from eye to collar, white throat and a rusty-brown breast band. Females and immatures are similar to Little Bunting but without chestnut head markings. Most have a rusty-brown breast band and streaks on the flanks which are diagnostic. Slight crest. Favours open wooded areas. Recorded twice during the 1975/76 winter but because of its abundance in the birdshops at that time the possibility of escapes could not be disregarded. Hong Kong is within this species' wintering range and due to the drabness of females and immatures may be overlooked.

[**REED BUNTING** *Emberiza schoeniclus* 藍鵐
not illustrated
6". Vagrant. Breeding male has distinctive black head and throat with white moustache stripe and prominent white collar. Females and immatures are like large Little Buntings without chestnut head markings. One record from Mai Po, March 1975. Possibly overlooked.
DB]

STRAM'S
UNTING

MASKED
BUNTING

♂

♀

REY-HEADED
BUNTING

breeding

YELLOW-BREASTED
BUNTING

♀

♂

CHESTNUT
BUNTING

♀

CHESTNUT BUNTING

♂

LITTLE BUNTING

Karan Phillipps

CRESTED BUNTING AND MUNIAS

CRESTED BUNTING *Melophus lathami* 栗鵐

6½". Resident.* Male unmistakable. Female has shorter crest but always chestnut on the wings. Active and bold. Often perches on overhead wires. Call is a repeated 'pit-pit.' In spring and summer is common on the upper slopes of hills where it breeds. In winter comes down to cultivated lowlands, occasionally in large flocks. The nest is built on the ground or in a cleft in a rock. The breeding season is from April to June and the usual clutch is four or five eggs.

MUNIAS

Small round-bodied birds with thick conical bills. Gregarious. Flight is direct and rapid. Build globular nests of plant fibres with side entrances.

CHESTNUT MUNIA *Lonchura malacca* 栗腹文雀

4½". Summer visitor.* The race *atricapilla* breeds on the Deep Bay Marshes and is seen there quite commonly between March and October, sometimes in flocks of up to 60 in autumn. Winter records and sightings elsewhere are rare. Immatures are pale earth brown, lighter below. The call is a shrill 'peep' 'peep'. The Three-Coloured Munia (race *malacca*) has been seen on about five occasions, always single birds and usually in the company of the nominate race. These latter birds are almost certainly escapes as this race does not normally occur in China.

SPOTTED MUNIA *Lonchura punctulata* 斑文雀

4½". Resident.* Scaly breast and underparts are diagnostic but often difficult to see. Immatures are plain brown, buffy below without scaling. Call is a repeated 'chit-it' 'chit-it.' Move in compact flocks like a swarm of bees. Feed in rice-fields, often with White-Backed Munias and Tree Sparrows, and are undoubtedly a serious pest. Widespread and locally common, being found almost anywhere except dense woodland. A large conspicuous nest is constructed in a tree. Often several are built and not used. The breeding season is from March to August and six or seven eggs is the usual clutch.

WHITE-HEADED MUNIA *Lonchura maja* 白腰文鳥

4½". Escape. White head is diagnostic. Immatures are separated from similar Chestnut Munias by paler head than rest of body. Odd birds are fairly frequently reported but are regarded as escapes as Hong Kong is well north of this species' normal range.

WHITE-BACKED MUNIA *Lonchura striata* 白腰文雀

4½". Resident.* Pointed black tail is diagnostic. Immatures are paler and the rump is only buffy-white. Thin trilling call. Usually seen in small flocks. Widespread. Found in almost any open habitat including urban gardens. Appears to have increased considerably in recent years and is now locally common in the New Territories and on Hong Kong Island. Breeding has only been proved in the last few years.

RED AVADAVAT *Amandava amandava* 紅梅花雀

4". Resident. Adult male unmistakable. Immatures lack red rump and distinctive wing spots. Call note is a shrill 'chirp.' Origins are uncertain as this is a common cagebird but certainly appears to be established in the Deep Bay area and Long Valley where flocks of up to 35 have occurred. Breeding has not been proved but birds have been seen carrying nesting material. Occasionally recorded elsewhere, usually where there is a stand of tall grass.

[**BAYA WEAVER** *Ploceus philippinus* 黃胸織布鳥
not illustrated

6". Escape. A brown streaked, finch-like bird with heavy bill, black mask and bright yellow crown. Females and immatures lack distinctive black and yellow markings but should be identified by the heavy bill. Occasionally seen in large flocks of 'escaped birds.']

CRESTED BUNTING ♂

CRESTED BUNTING ♀

SPOTTED MUNIA
adult

CHESTNUT
MUNIA
adult

CHESTNUT MUNIA
(Three-Coloured Munia)

WHITE-HEADED
MUNIA
adult

WHITE-BACKED MUNIA
adult

RED AVADAVAT ♀

RED AVADAVAT ♂

List of Vagrant Species

These are birds which have been recorded in an apparently wild state in Hong Kong and which are not otherwise mentioned in the text.

SPECIES	SCIENTIFIC NAME	LAST RECORDED
Red-Throated Diver	Gavia stellata	1966 (3)
Red-Necked Grebe	Podiceps grisegena	1955 (1)
Swinhoe's Storm-Petrel	Oceanodroma monorhis	1961 (1)
Streaked Shearwater	Calonectris leucomelas	1977 (1)
Christmas Island Frigate-Bird	Fregata andrewsi	1976 (2)
Von Schrenck's Little Bittern	Ixobrychus eurhythmus	1957 (4)
Japanese Night Heron	Gorsachius goisagi	1977 (3)
Baikal Teal	Anas formosa	1961 (2)
Mandarin	Aix galericulata	1976 (4)
Common Pochard	Aythya ferina	1970 (1)
Goldeneye	Bucephala clangula	1973 (3)
Chinese Goshawk	Accipiter soloensis	1977 (4)
Hen Harrier	Circus cyaneus	1977 (?)
Ring-Necked Pheasant	Phasianus colchicus	1904 extinct
Yellow-Legged Button-Quail	Turnix tanki	1974 (?)
Baillon's Crake	Porzana pusilla	1966 (4)
Oystercatcher	Haematopus ostralegus	1958 (1)
Long-Billed Plover	Charadrius placidus	1955 (1)
Solitary Snipe	Gallinago solitaria	1974 (2)
Jack Snipe	Lymnocryptes minimus	1970 (3)
Nordmann's Greenshank	Tringa guttifer	1971 (2)
Common Gull	Larus canus	1975 (2)
Slaty-Backed Gull	Larus schistisagus	1970 (5)
Glaucous Gull	Larus hyperboreus	1974 (1)
Great Black-Headed Gull	Larus ichthyaetus	1977 (2)
Pomarine Skua	Stercorarius pomarinus	1957 (1)
Long-Tailed Skua	Stercorarius longicaudus	1976 (1)
Ancient Auk	Synthliboramphus antiquus	1975 (1)
Bar-Tailed Cuckoo-Dove	Macropygia unchall	1960 (1)
Hodgson's Hawk-Cuckoo	Cuculus fugax	1971 (1)
Drongo-Cuckoo	Surniculus lugubris	1971 (1)
Scops Owl	Otus scops	1969 (5)
Long-Eared Owl	Asio otus	1962 (2)
Short-Eared Owl	Asio flammeus	1977 (2)
Brown Hawk-Owl	Ninox scutulata	1968 (4)
Chestnut-Cheeked Starling	Sturnus philippensis	1976 (1)
Greater Cuckoo-Shrike	Coracina novaehollandiae	1962 (1)
Rosy Minivet	Pericrocotus roseus	1968 (1)
White-Bellied Yuhina	Yuhina zantholeuca	1953 (1)
Sulphur-Breasted Warbler	Phylloscopus ricketti	1974 (6)
Golden-Spectacled Warbler	Seicercus burkii	1977 (2)
Chestnut-Crowned Warbler	Seicercus castaniceps	1972 (1)

SPECIES	SCIENTIFIC NAME	LAST RECORDED
Rufous-Faced Warbler	*Abroscopus albogularis*	1964 (2)
Red-Headed Tit	*Aegithalos concinnus*	1977 (2)
Petchora Pipit	*Anthus gustavi*	1971 (1)
Yellow-Browed Bunting	*Emberiza chrysophrys*	1977 (2)
Japanese Yellow Bunting	*Emberiza sulphurata*	1860 (1)

The figures in brackets denote the number of times the species has been recorded.

SHORT-EARED OWL   *Asio Flammeus*

Bibliography

The principal works consulted in the preparation of this book are listed below. Those which are most useful to bird watchers in Hong Kong are marked with an asterisk.

Bertel Bruun. 1970. *The Hamlyn Guide to Birds of Britain and Europe.* Hamlyn, London.

Boonsong Lekagul and Edward W. Cronin Jr. 1974 (2nd Edition). *Bird Guide of Thailand.* Association for the Conservation of Wildlife, Bangkok. Fully illustrated.

Cheng Tso-hsin. 1976 (revised edition). *Distributional List of Chinese Birds.* Peking Institute of Zoology, Academia Sinica. Text is in Chinese.

*H. Heinzel, R. Fitter and J. Parslow. 1972. *The Birds of Britain and Europe with North Africa and the Middle East.* Collins, London. Covers many species which migrate through or winter in Hong Kong.

*G. A. C. Herklots. 1967 (2nd edition). *Hong Kong Birds.* South China Morning Post, Hong Kong. Few illustrations but contains useful notes and descriptions.

*Hong Kong Bird Watching Society. 1958–1975. *The Hong Kong Bird Report* (published annually). Annual systematic list plus useful articles.

*B. F. King, E. C. Dickinson and M. Woodcock. 1975. *A Field Guide to the Birds of South-East Asia.* Collins, London. The major current work for the region – indispensable.

K. Kobayashi. 1963. *Birds of Japan in Natural Colours.* Hoikusha, Osaka. Good illustrations, but text is in Japanese.

J. D. D. La Touche. 1925–1934. *A Handbook of the Birds of Eastern China.* Taylor & Francis, London. 2 vols. Rare and expensive. Classic work with excellent detailed descriptions.

R. T. Peterson, G. Mountfort and P. A. D. Hollom. 1974 (3rd edition). *A Field Guide to the Birds of Britain and Europe.* Collins, London.

B. E. Smythies. 1968 (2nd edition). *The Birds of Borneo.* Oliver & Boyd, London. Out of print and difficult to obtain.

*M. A. Webster. 1975. *An Annotated Checklist of the Birds of Hong Kong.* Hong Kong Bird Watching Society. A comprehensive checklist.

*M. A. Webster. 1972. *Check-List of the Birds of Hong Kong.* Swiss Worldwide Ltd, $HK1.00. A useful pocket-sized list of Hong Kong birds recorded up to 1972. Obtainable through the Hong Kong Bird Watching Society.

*M. A. Webster and K. Phillipps. 1976. *A New Guide to the Birds of Hong Kong.* Sino-American, Hong Kong. Covers every species found in Hong Kong up to 1976 but few illustrations are in colour.

Index of Scientific Names

GREAT TIT *Parus major*

Index of English Names

BLACK KITE *Milvus migrans*

Clive Viney. A Chartered Surveyor who arrived in Hong Kong from the United Kingdom in 1967 to take up a post with the Public Works Department. He has always had an active interest in natural history and was elected Honorary Recorder of The Hong Kong Birdwatching Society in 1975 and is a major contributor to *'The Hong Kong Bird Report'* (Published annually).

Karen Phillipps. Born and brought up in Malaysia. She trained as an illustrator in London and has lived in Hong Kong since 1972. Previously published works include *'A New Guide to the Birds of Hong Kong'.* Her work has been exhibited in various galleries in Hong Kong. Currently she is working on a *'Colour Guide to Animal Life in Hong Kong'.*

KWANGTUNG PROVINCE

DEEP BAY

Sham Chun
Man Kam To
Lo Wu
CREST HILL
Long Valley
Ho Sheung Heung
Lok Ma Chau
SHEUNG SHUI
SHEK WU HUI
SAN TIN
Ditts Corner
GOLF COURSE
FANLING
Tam Kon Chau
Tai Shang Wai
Mai Po Marshes
Mai Po
Lin Tong Mei
PAK TAI TO YAN
Tsim Bei Tsui Police Post
Mong Tseng Peninsula
LAU FAU SHAN
San Tin San Wai
Ying Pun
Pok Wai
KAI KEUNG LENG
TAI TO YAN
Sha Kong Tsuen
Sha Kong Wai
WANG CHAU
Ponds
Ngau Hom Sha
San Wai
PING SHAN
Sha Po
Shui Tau
PAT HEUNG
TAI MO SHAN 958
SH PLA
HA TSUEN
YUEN LONG
Au Tau
KAM TIN
Shui Tsiu San Tsuen
Yuen Kong
SHEK KONG
Kwun Yam Keng
Nim Wan
Hung Shui Kiu
Tsz Long
Kap Lung
Tai Shui Hang
Tuen Tsz Wai
Ho Pui
Twisk
Tsang Kok
LamTei
Tai Tong
CHEUN Lung
URMSTON ROAD
TUEN MUN
Wong Fung Leng
Sheung Fa Shan
Lung Kwu Tan
CASTLE PEAK 583
Sam Shing Hui
Tai Lam Chung Reservoir
Tsing ai Tong
TSUEN WAN
Siu Lang Shui
TAI LAM CHUNG
SHAM TSENG
KWAI CHUNG
Kowl Resel
Lung Kwu Chau
Pearl Island
Tsing Lung Tau
Ma Wan
TSING YI
Tree Island
The Brothers
Kap Shui Mun
Luk Keng
TSING CHAU
Stonecu Island
Sha Chau
Chek Lap Kok Island
Mong Tung Hang
Sham Shui Kok
Sz Pak
Green Island
San Tau
Ngau Kwu Long
DISCOVERY BAY
Peng Chau
Kau Yi Chau
Fui Yiu Ha
Nim Shue Wan
VICTORI PEAK 554
Sai Tso Wan
SHAM SHEK TSUEN
TUNG CHUNG
TAI SHUI HANG
MUI WO
Pok Fu Lam
ABER
LANTAU ISLAND
SILVER MINE BAY
Sunshine Island
TAI O
NGONG PING
Shap Long Tsuen
Hei Ling Chau
Lee
KEUNG SHAN
LANTAU PEAK 934
SUNSET PEAK 869
San Shek Wan
CHI MA WAN PENINSULA
EAST LAMMA CHANNEL
Man Cheung Po
Cheung Sha
Yung Shue Wan
YI O
Shek Pik Reservoir
Tong Fuk
Cheung Chau
Sok Kwu Wan
Tai Long Wan
Shui Hau
TONG FUK MIU WAN
WEST LAMMA CHANNEL
Tsin Yue Wan
Shek Kwu Chau
LAMMA ISLAND
FAN LAU
Tai A Chau
Soko Islands
Siu A Chau

Scale

Km 0   2   4   6   8   10   12   14 Km